Proficiency in the Sentence Writing Strategy*

STUDENT LESSONS, VOLUME 1

Jan B. Sheldon, Ph.D.
Jean B. Schumaker, Ph.D.

Edge Enterprises, Inc.
P.O. Box 1304
Lawrence, Kansas
Revised Edition, 1998

*Formerly titled The Sentence Writing Strategy

Copy Editor: Jean B. Schumaker
Cover Design: Mike Bingham
Internal Design: John B. Naughtin

First edition, 15th Printing 2012
Copyright © 1995 by Jan Sheldon and Jean B. Schumaker, 717 Ohio Street, Lawrence, Kansas 66044

CONTENTS

ACKNOWLEDGMENTS

The conceptualization, development, validation, and revision of the *Learning Strategies Curriculum* has benefited from the efforts of many individuals. We gratefully acknowledge the innumerable contributions of the following colleagues and professionals: Vickie Beals, Jean Brownlee, Fran Clark, Pegi Denton, Keren Hamburger, Keith Lenz, Ann Hoffman, Sue Nolan, John Schmidt, Conn Thomas, Mike Warner, and Ginger Williams. Additionally, the personnel of the Lawrence School District have been tremendous allies during the past eight-year period of development and research on the *Learning Strategies Curriculum*. Specifically, we wish to credit and thank Carol Ann Buller, Steve Carlson, Ed Ellis, Don Herbel, Jerry Keimig, Karen Lyerla, Bruce Passman, Brad Tate, and Tony Van Reusen.

The *Proficiency in the Sentence Writing Strategy* student lessons were originally developed and field-tested in 1974 in a summer school program for junior-high students. We are grateful to our colleague, Dr. Jim Sherman, to the teachers, Burleigh Smith and Bob Sharkey, and to the students for their valuable help in this original development effort.

In the eleven years since then, the students who participated in the original field test have graduated from high school (and some from college), the accompanying *Instructor's Manual* has been developed and field-tested, and the Student Lessons have been much improved. We deeply appreciate the many suggestions made by Susan Dent, Don Deshler, Pegi Denton, and Pat Jonason regarding improvements to be made throughout the lesson materials. We also appreciate the critiques provided by countless teachers across the nation who have used the lessons since the original field test.

JS, JBS

INTRODUCTION

The materials in this book are designed to be used in conjunction with instruction that is described in the *Proficiency in the Sentence Writing Strategy Instructor's Manual.** They are not designed to be used in absence of this instruction, nor are they to be used without regard for mastery learning.

Permission is granted to the owner of this book to copy the quizzes and lessons for personal use in providing instruction to students learning *Proficiency in the Sentence Writing Strategy.* Copying these lesson materials for other instructors or any other purpose in any form is in violation of copyright law.

*Schumaker, J.B., & Sheldon, J. (1985). *Proficiency in the Sentence Writing Strategy Instructor's Manual.* Lawrence: The University of Kansas. (3061 Dole, University of Kansas, Lawrence, KS 66045.)

SIMPLE SENTENCES

QUIZ AND LESSONS

SIMPLE SENTENCE QUIZ

Name_____

Date_____

INSTRUCTIONS: Read the information, and fill in the blanks.

● **The sentence is the basic unit of communication. One type of sentence is the <u>simple sentence.</u>**

☐   1.   A simple sentence has _____ independent clause(s).

                                                    (How many?)

● **An <u>independent clause</u> always has two important parts.**

☐   2.   The part that names what the sentence is about is called the _____ .

☐   3.   The part that tells the action or state of being is called the _____ .

● **The <u>subject</u> of a sentence names the person, place, thing, quality, or idea the sentence is about.**

Example Sentence #1: Snow melts.

☐   4.   The subject of Example Sentence #1 is _____ .

● **The <u>verb</u> (or predicate) of a sentence tells the action or state of being of the subject.**

Example Sentence #2: Water runs.

☐   5.   The verb in Example Sentence #2 is _____ .

● **The <u>main subject</u> is the one word that names what the sentence is about.**

Example Sentence #3: The fluffy white kitten squeezed under the porch.

☐   6.   The main subject in Example Sentence #3 is _____ .

SIMPLE SENTENCE QUIZ (Continued)

Name_____

● **The <u>complete verb</u> includes the main verb (that shows the action) and any helping verbs.**

Example Sentence #4: The children are playing with a ball.

7. The complete verb in this sentence is _____ _____ .

● **The subject generally comes <u>before</u> the verb in a simple sentence.**

Example Sentence #5: The rain fell gently.

8. The verb of Example Sentence #5 is _____ .

9. The subject comes before the verb of this sentence.
   The subject in Example Sentence #5 is _____ .

● **The subject can come <u>after</u> the verb in a simple sentence.**

Example Sentence #6: Here are the shoes.

10. The verb of Example Sentence #6 is _____ .

11. The subject comes after the verb of this sentence.
    The subject in Example Sentence #6 is _____ .

● **The subject can come <u>between</u> the helping verb and the main verb in a simple sentence.**

Example Sentence #7: Is Candy coming?

12. The complete verb of Example Sentence #7 is _____ _____ .

13. The subject of Example Sentence #7 is _____ .

SIMPLE SENTENCE QUIZ (Continued)

Name_____

- **A simple sentence may have a compound subject. A compound subject means that there is more than one subject in the sentence.**

  <u>Matt</u> and <u>James</u> are the two subjects that make up the compound subject in this
  S   S
  sentence: *Matt and James dived into the water.*

Mark each of the main subjects in these sentences with an "S."

☐	☐	14. The dogs and cats ran in circles.
☐	☐ ☐	15. Scott, Bill, and Jeff went to the beach.
☐	☐	16. The old man and his grandson took a walk together.

- **A simple sentence may also have a compound verb. A compound verb means that there is more than one verb in the sentence.**

  <u>Dived</u> and <u>jumped</u> are the two verbs that comprise the compound verb in this
  V   V
  sentence: *Steve dived and jumped into the water.*

Mark each of the verbs in these sentences with a "V."

☐	☐	17. The dogs barked and yelped all night.
☐	☐	18. Jan read and graded the quizzes.
☐	☐	19. The girl gulped her breakfast and dashed to school.

- **A simple sentence can have a compound subject and a compound verb.**

  For example, in the following sentence there are two subjects (marked with an "S") and two verbs (marked with a "V"):
  S   S   V   V
  The men and women took their places and waited for the signal to begin.

Mark each main subject in this sentence with an "S" and each verb with a "V."

☐	☐	20. The witches and their black cats surrounded the kettle and looked at the sky.
☐	☐	

SIMPLE SENTENCE LESSON 1A

Name_____

Date_____

INSTRUCTIONS:
1. Do the "S" Step of the "PENS" Strategy to check each sentence.
2. Mark the complete verb(s) in each sentence with a "V."
3. Mark the main subject(s) in each sentence with an "S."
4. In the blank to the left of the sentence, write the correct sentence formula for the sentence. Choose the correct formula from your Formula Card.

EXAMPLE:

_SV_   0. The big bear was standing on top of the picnic table.

F   V   S   Formulas

☐ ☐ ☐ _____   1. The old man walked slowly down the street.

☐ ☐ ☐ _____   2. The boys and girls were running around.

☐ ☐ ☐ _____   3. A mean dog chased and bit the girl.

☐ ☐ ☐ _____   4. The little girl ran quickly home.

☐ ☐ ☐ _____   5. The mother and father came out of the house and comforted the girl.

☐ ☐ ☐ _____   6. The father called the dogcatcher and chased the dog.

☐ ☐ ☐ _____   7. He and another man finally caught the dog.

☐ ☐ ☐ _____   8. There are dry leaves and branches on the ground.

☐ ☐ ☐ _____   9. Chicago is located on Lake Michigan and has one of the busiest airports.

☐ ☐ ☐ _____   10. Bravery and courage are shown by heroes and often are found in a moment of crisis.

SIMPLE SENTENCE LESSON 1B

Name_____

Date_____

INSTRUCTIONS:
1. **Do the "S" Step of the "PENS" Strategy to check each sentence.**
2. **Mark the complete verb(s) in each sentence with a "V."**
3. **Mark the main subject(s) in each sentence with an "S."**
4. **In the blank to the left of the sentence, write the correct sentence formula for the sentence. Choose the correct formula from your Formula Card.**

EXAMPLE:

              S   V

_SV_   0. The big bear was standing on top of the picnic table.

F   V   S   Formulas

☐ ☐ ☐ _____ 1. The girls went to school early and left late.

☐ ☐ ☐ _____ 2. The happy man and woman were married last Friday.

☐ ☐ ☐ _____ 3. The dishonesty of the young man disgusted the members of the jury.

☐ ☐ ☐ _____ 4. Jeff and Rick threw the ball and caught it.

☐ ☐ ☐ _____ 5. Kathy and Bill went to the movie and ate popcorn.

☐ ☐ ☐ _____ 6. The horse jumped and kicked Scott.

☐ ☐ ☐ _____ 7. London has become famous for its thick fogs and often has rainy weather.

☐ ☐ ☐ _____ 8. The angry man and woman yelled at the young child.

☐ ☐ ☐ _____ 9. National parks are scattered through the states and attract thousands of visitors each year.

☐ ☐ ☐ _____ 10. There go Scott and James.

SIMPLE SENTENCE LESSON 1C

Name_____

Date_____

INSTRUCTIONS:
1. Do the "S" Step of the "PENS" Strategy to check each sentence.
2. Mark the complete verb(s) in each sentence with a "V."
3. Mark the main subject(s) in each sentence with an "S."
4. In the blank to the left of the sentence, write the correct sentence formula for the sentence. Choose the correct formula from your Formula Card.

EXAMPLE:

           S   V

__SV__   0. The big bear was standing on top of the picnic table.

F   V   S   Formulas

☐ ☐ ☐   1. The pie and cookies disappeared last night.

☐ ☐ ☐   2. The boy ate the food and got a stomachache.

☐ ☐ ☐   3. You and James could come over tonight.

☐ ☐ ☐   4. The people at the party danced and ate a lot.

☐ ☐ ☐   5. Here come the paperboy and the milkman.

☐ ☐ ☐   6. The success of this meeting will be decided by the final vote.

☐ ☐ ☐   7. Mary and I are sick of the whole thing and want you to stop.

☐ ☐ ☐   8. Chip went to Boston with Don.

☐ ☐ ☐   9. Illness and loneliness are problems for many older people.

☐ ☐ ☐   10. Rick and his girlfriend had an argument and walked angrily away from each other.

SIMPLE SENTENCE LESSON 1D

Name _____

Date _____

INSTRUCTIONS:
1. Do the "S" Step of the "PENS" Strategy to check each sentence.
2. Mark the complete verb(s) in each sentence with a "V."
3. Mark the main subject(s) in each sentence with an "S."
4. In the blank to the left of the sentence, write the correct sentence formula for the sentence. Choose the correct formula from your Formula Card.

EXAMPLE:

             S   V

SV   0. The big bear was standing on top of the picnic table.

F V S   Formulas

☐ ☐ ☐   _____   1. I should have a pet white rabbit at home.

☐ ☐ ☐   _____   2. The shiny beetles could have flown five miles and landed on some trees.

☐ ☐ ☐   _____   3. Down dived the blue plane toward the earth.

☐ ☐ ☐   _____   4. Beauty is in the eye of the beholder and can be misjudged easily.

☐ ☐ ☐   _____   5. France and England had many disputes and fought for decades.

☐ ☐ ☐   _____   6. The spaceman and his friends sipped their lunch through tubes.

☐ ☐ ☐   _____   7. My older brother sleeps with a pillow on his head.

☐ ☐ ☐   _____   8. The green snake and the brown toad were not close friends.

☐ ☐ ☐   _____   9. Jonathan and Maria ate a pizza and drank pop.

☐ ☐ ☐   _____   10. Fred threw a thirty-yard pass and blocked for the tight end.

SIMPLE SENTENCE LESSON 2A

Name_____

Date_____

INSTRUCTIONS:
1. **Make each of the following into a simple sentence that matches the listed formula.**
2. **Do the "S" Step of the "PENS" Strategy to check each sentence.**
3. **Mark each complete verb with a "V."**
4. **Mark each main subject with an "S."**

EXAMPLE:
(S VV) 0. The storm _toppled several trees and damaged our roof._

M   C   V&S   Formulas

☐ ☐ ☐ (S VV)   1. John _____

☐ ☐ ☐ (SS V)   2. The boy _____

☐ ☐ ☐ (S V)   3. The monkey _____

☐ ☐ ☐ (S VV)   4. Bob _____

☐ ☐ ☐ (S V)   5. The long branches of the tree _____

☐ ☐ ☐ (S V)   6. The soldier's bravery _____

☐ ☐ ☐ (SS VV) 7. Judy _____

☐ ☐ ☐ (S V)   8. The woods _____

☐ ☐ ☐ (SS V)   9. Lately, my friend _____

☐ ☐ ☐ (S VV) 10. Suddenly, the movie theatre _____

SIMPLE SENTENCE LESSON 2B

Name_____

Date_____

INSTRUCTIONS:
1. Make each of the following into a simple sentence that matches the listed formula.
2. Do the "S" Step of the "PENS" Strategy to check each sentence.
3. Mark each complete verb with a "V."
4. Mark each main subject with an "S."

EXAMPLE:	S V V
(S VV)	0. The storm _toppled several trees and damaged our roof._

M   C   V&S   Formulas

☐ ☐ ☐   (S VV)   1.   Jeff _____

_____

☐ ☐ ☐   (S VV)   2.   An apple _____

_____

☐ ☐ ☐   (S V)   3.   Tomorrow, I _____

_____

☐ ☐ ☐   (SS V)   4.   Anna _____

_____

☐ ☐ ☐   (S V)   5.   Texas _____

_____

☐ ☐ ☐   (S VV)   6.   The horse _____

_____

☐ ☐ ☐   (S V)   7.   Last night's victory _____

_____

☐ ☐ ☐   (SS VV)   8.   Hopefully, Don _____

_____

☐ ☐ ☐   (S V)   9.   The building _____

_____

☐ ☐ ☐   (SS V)   10.   You _____

_____

SIMPLE SENTENCE LESSON 2C

Name_____

Date_____

INSTRUCTIONS:
1. **Make each of the following into a simple sentence that matches the listed formula.**
2. **Do the "S" Step of the "PENS" Strategy to check each sentence.**
3. **Mark each complete verb with a "V."**
4. **Mark each main subject with an "S."**

EXAMPLE: (S VV)	0. The storm S V toppled several trees and V damaged our roof.

M	C	V&S	**Formulas**
☐	☐	☐	(SS VV) 1. Afterwards, Cathy _____
☐	☐	☐	(S VV) 2. My uncle _____
☐	☐	☐	(S V) 3. The day _____
☐	☐	☐	(SS V) 4. Harry _____
☐	☐	☐	(S V) 5. The lake _____
☐	☐	☐	(S VV) 6. Jason _____
☐	☐	☐	(S V) 7. Furthermore, honesty _____
☐	☐	☐	(SS V) 8. Unexpectedly, the phone _____
☐	☐	☐	(S V) 9. The old gray owl _____
☐	☐	☐	(S VV) 10. An ant _____

SIMPLE SENTENCE LESSON 2D

Name_____

Date_____

INSTRUCTIONS:
1. **Make each of the following into a simple sentence that matches the listed formula.**
2. **Do the "S" Step of the "PENS" Strategy to check each sentence.**
3. **Mark each complete verb with a "V."**
4. **Mark each main subject with an "S."**

EXAMPLE:
(S VV) 0. The storm *toppled several trees and damaged our roof.*

M	C	V&S	Formulas		
☐	☐	☐	(S V)	1.	The haunted house _____
☐	☐	☐	(SS V)	2.	Recently, my mother _____
☐	☐	☐	(S V)	3.	An ambulance _____
☐	☐	☐	(S VV)	4.	J. C. Kelly _____
☐	☐	☐	(S V)	5.	Happiness _____
☐	☐	☐	(S VV)	6.	Alaska _____
☐	☐	☐	(S V)	7.	After lunch, she _____
☐	☐	☐	(SS V)	8.	Suddenly, the wind _____
☐	☐	☐	(S V)	9.	Gracefully, the bird _____
☐	☐	☐	(SS VV)	10.	Tom _____

15

SIMPLE SENTENCE LESSON 3A, 3B, 3C, 3D (circle one)

Name_____

Date_____

INSTRUCTIONS:
1. **For the first eight sentences, write a simple sentence that matches each of the listed formulas.**
2. **For the last two sentences, choose a formula from your Formula Card. Write the formula on the blank to the left of the sentence. Use the "PENS" Strategy to write a sentence that matches the formula you have chosen.**
3. **Be sure to use the "S" Step of the "PENS" Strategy to check your work.**

EXAMPLE:
(SS V)   0. $\underset{S}{\text{The oranges}}$ and $\underset{S}{\text{apples}}$ on the trees $\underset{V}{\text{looked}}$ delicious.

M   C   Formulas

☐ ☐   (S V)   1. _____

☐ ☐   (S VV)   2. _____

☐ ☐   (SS V)   3. _____

☐ ☐   (SS VV)   4. _____

☐ ☐   (S V)   5. _____

☐ ☐   (SS VV)   6. _____

☐ ☐   (S VV)   7. _____

☐ ☐   (SS VV)   8. _____

☐ ☐   _____   9. _____

☐ ☐   _____   10. _____

SIMPLE SENTENCE LESSON 4A, 4B, 4C, 4D (circle one)

Name_____

Date_____

INSTRUCTIONS:

1. In the space below, use the "PENS" Strategy to write at least six sentences about the topic listed on your Assignment Sheet. Include in this group of sentences at least one of each of the four kinds of simple sentences. Use your Formula Card for reference as needed.

2. Use the "S" Step of the "PENS" Strategy and a *Simple Sentence Checklist* to check the kinds and number of simple sentences you have written.

3. Attach your completed *Simple Sentence Checklist* to this sheet when you are done.

Topic: _____

_____

_____

_____

_____

_____

_____

_____

_____

_____

_____

_____

_____

_____

_____

_____

_____

_____

_____

_____

_____

_____

COMPOUND SENTENCES

QUIZ AND LESSONS

COMPOUND SENTENCE QUIZ

Name_____

Date_____

> **INSTRUCTIONS:** Read the information, and fill in the blanks.

● **The sentence is a basic unit of communication.**

☐   1.   A simple sentence has _____ independent clause(s).
                                    (How many?)

☐   2.   A compound sentence has _____ or more independent clauses.
                                    (How many?)

● **An <u>independent clause</u> always has two important parts.**

☐   3.   The part that names the person, place, thing, quality, or idea that the sentence is about is called the _____ .

☐   4.   The part that shows the action or state of being is called the _____ .

● **A <u>compound sentence</u> contains more than one <u>independent clause</u>.**

Example Sentence #1: Helen helped, but Mary refused.

The two independent clauses in Example Sentence #1 are:

☐   5.   _____ .

☐   6.   _____ .

Example Sentence #2: Lee teaches math, and his wife teaches history.

● **The two independent clauses in Example Sentence #2 are:**

☐   7.   _____ .

☐   8.   _____ .

● **Independent clauses in compound sentences can be joined by a <u>comma</u> and a <u>coordinating conjunction</u>. The most common coordinating conjunctions are <u>for, and, nor, but, or, yet,</u> and <u>so</u>.**

Put the <u>best</u> conjunction in each of the following sentences. (Use each conjunction <u>one</u> time.)

☐   9.   I like Bill, _____ sometimes he is too loud.

☐   10.   The cat and dog raced around the yard, _____ they hated each other.

☐	11. The food got cold, _____ they heated it up.
☐	12. Mrs. Planter went to the butcher shop, _____ she bought a sirloin steak.
☐	13. The milk was not on the counter, _____ was it on the table.
☐	14. Put that back, _____ I will call the cops.
☐	15. She seems like a nice person, _____ she has no friends.

● **When two independent clauses in a compound sentence are joined by a coordinating conjunction, a <u>comma</u> is usually placed right before the conjunction.**

Put a comma in the proper place in each of the following sentences:

16. The clerk rang up the sale and his helper packed the groceries.
17. The children played tag but they did not include Steven.
18. By mistake, the ice man turned down the freezer so all the ice melted.
19. I invited Kathy for she is my best friend.

● **Independent clauses may also be joined by a <u>semicolon</u> (;) when there is no coordinating conjunction.**

Put a semicolon between the independent clauses in each of the following sentences:

20. Dr. Lee teaches math his wife teaches history.
21. The salmon swam upstream they were headed for their home.
22. Potatoes and beans were served the taste was terrible.
23. The snow finally is melting it has been on the ground for two weeks.

● **An independent clause must be able to stand alone. Do not mistake a simple sentence with compound subjects and/or compound verbs for a compound sentence.**

Put a comma in the proper place in each sentence that has two independent clauses. Do not add a comma to sentences that have only one independent clause.

24. The water rose and then receded.
25. The bird rose rapidly and headed west.
26. The tree fell and the lumberjack stripped the branches from its trunk.
27. Her dress was green and her gloves were white.
28. She wore a green dress and white gloves.
29. The Angels got creamed by the Devils for the Devils are a better team.
30. The Angels played the Devils and lost.

COMPOUND SENTENCE LESSON 1A

Name_____

Date_____

INSTRUCTIONS:
1. Do the "S" Step of the "PENS" Strategy on each sentence.
2. Mark each complete verb in each sentence with a "V."
3. Mark each main subject in each sentence with an "S."
4. In the blank to the left of the sentence, write the correct sentence formula for the sentence. Choose the correct formula from your Formula Card.

EXAMPLE:

　　　　　　　S　V　　　　　　　　　S　　V
I,cI　　0. We had to give up, for the rope continued to break.

F	V	S	Formulas		
☐	☐	☐	_____	1.	The snow was falling, and the wind was howling.
☐	☐	☐	_____	2.	Nothing could be done; the cold air had frozen the door shut.
☐	☐	☐	_____	3.	Jake got a crowbar; Mac grabbed a shovel.
☐	☐	☐	_____	4.	The pair pounded on the ice, but it would not crack.
☐	☐	☐	_____	5.	Finally, Jenna lit a fire near the door, so the ice would melt.
☐	☐	☐	_____	6.	The friends had to get the door open soon, or they would freeze to death.
☐	☐	☐	_____	7.	They were shivering; the temperature was 15 degrees below zero.
☐	☐	☐	_____	8.	Jenna could not bend her fingers, nor could she feel her toes.
☐	☐	☐	_____	9.	Jake pried the door open, and they rushed inside.
☐	☐	☐	_____	10.	The group made a fire in the fireplace, for they needed to thaw out.

COMPOUND SENTENCE LESSON 1B

Name_____

Date_____

INSTRUCTIONS:
1. **Do the "S" Step of the "PENS" Strategy on each sentence.**
2. **Mark each complete verb in each sentence with a "V."**
3. **Mark each main subject in each sentence with an "S."**
4. **In the blank to the left of the sentence, write the correct sentence formula for the sentence. Choose the correct formula from your Formula Card.**

EXAMPLE:

        S   V   S   V

I, c I   0. We had to give up, for the rope continued to break.

F   V   S   Formulas

☐ ☐ ☐ _____ 1. Michel and Burdett went for a hike; the day was beautiful.

☐ ☐ ☐ _____ 2. The sun was shining, and the sky was clear.

☐ ☐ ☐ _____ 3. The hikers soon were lost, for they had forgotten the map.

☐ ☐ ☐ _____ 4. Michel seemed scared, but Burdett showed courage.

☐ ☐ ☐ _____ 5. The couple climbed to the mountaintop, so they could see the view and get their bearings.

☐ ☐ ☐ _____ 6. Michel unpacked the food; Burdett started the fire.

☐ ☐ ☐ _____ 7. The climbers were starving, yet they saved some food for the next day.

☐ ☐ ☐ _____ 8. The pair started down the mountain; the sun was high in the sky.

☐ ☐ ☐ _____ 9. Before long they found the path; it was hidden in the underbrush.

☐ ☐ ☐ _____ 10. The sportsmen got home at sunset, for their hike had taken all day.

COMPOUND SENTENCE LESSON 1C

Name_____

Date_____

INSTRUCTIONS:
1. **Do the "S" Step of the "PENS" Strategy on each sentence.**
2. **Mark each complete verb in each sentence with a "V."**
3. **Mark each main subject in each sentence with an "S."**
4. **In the blank to the left of the sentence, write the correct sentence formula for the sentence. Choose the correct formula from your Formula Card.**

EXAMPLE:

   S   V   S   V
I,cI   0. We had to give up, for the rope continued to break.

F	V	S	Formulas		
☐	☐	☐	_____	1.	The pool opens this weekend; we should go and grab some rays.
☐	☐	☐	_____	2.	Terry hates to change now, for she always uses the typewriter.
☐	☐	☐	_____	3.	The President called a meeting; he wants to stop the invasion.
☐	☐	☐	_____	4.	Scott took his college tests last month, yet he has not heard anything about the results.
☐	☐	☐	_____	5.	We should go to the all-you-can-eat pizza place; they have cheap food.
☐	☐	☐	_____	6.	The boys' basketball team is undefeated, and the girls' team seems to be on a winning streak.
☐	☐	☐	_____	7.	We could play video games, or we could stay here and listen to music.
☐	☐	☐	_____	8.	Jennifer's parents bought her a car, but they refuse to let her drive it with friends.
☐	☐	☐	_____	9.	Play practice starts in ten minutes, so you should hurry.
☐	☐	☐	_____	10.	Tina will graduate in the spring; she wants to join the Peace Corps and to work with people living in poor nations.

COMPOUND SENTENCE LESSON 1D

Name_____

Date_____

INSTRUCTIONS:
1. **Do the "S" Step of the "PENS" Strategy on each sentence.**
2. **Mark each complete verb in each sentence with a "V."**
3. **Mark each main subject in each sentence with an "S."**
4. **In the blank to the left of the sentence, write the correct sentence formula for the sentence. Choose the correct formula from your Formula Card.**

EXAMPLE:

$$\underline{I, c I}$$

        S V   S   V

0. We had to give up, for the rope continued to break.

F   V   S   Formulas

☐ ☐ ☐ _____ 1. The game is on Friday night; our team finally got into the playoffs.

☐ ☐ ☐ _____ 2. Chris asked Sarah to the Valentine's dance; she turned him down and is going with Ricky.

☐ ☐ ☐ _____ 3. Carrie wants to go to the movies with us, but she agreed to babysit for Mrs. Kelly.

☐ ☐ ☐ _____ 4. The fire was caused by the candles, or it began with a careless match.

☐ ☐ ☐ _____ 5. We saw the film on nuclear war, and it was very realistic.

☐ ☐ ☐ _____ 6. Those cars are so expensive; I will never be able to afford one!

☐ ☐ ☐ _____ 7. I have been looking for a job, yet I cannot find one.

☐ ☐ ☐ _____ 8. Our town got six inches of snow last night, so school was cancelled for the first time this year.

☐ ☐ ☐ _____ 9. People are starving in Africa; we need to send them food and money.

☐ ☐ ☐ _____ 10. Marilyn's parents will not allow her to go out this weekend, nor will they allow her to talk on the phone.

COMPOUND SENTENCE LESSON 2A

Name_____

Date_____

INSTRUCTIONS:

1. Complete each of the following sentences to make a compound sentence by adding an independent clause. Match your sentence to the listed formula, and use the conjunction in parentheses if one is required. Be sure to include a comma or semicolon in each sentence.
2. Do the "S" Step of the "PENS" Strategy to the clause you have added to the sentence.
3. Mark each complete verb in your added clause with a "V."
4. Mark each main subject in your added clause with an "S."

EXAMPLE:

I,cI   0.   We could not see the stars, <u>nor could we see the moon.</u>

(nor)

M	C	V&S	Formulas & Conjunctions		
☐	☐	☐	I,cI (and)	1.	Scott rode his moped to school _____
☐	☐	☐	I;I	2.	Jeff wanted to leave early _____
☐	☐	☐	I,cI (but)	3.	The President called for peace _____
☐	☐	☐	I,cI (so)	4.	Rita earned $99 dollars _____
☐	☐	☐	I;I	5.	Happiness cannot be bought _____
☐	☐	☐	I,cI (or)	6.	You will finish your work now _____
☐	☐	☐	I;I	7.	The bus leaves promptly at 8:30 A.M. _____
☐	☐	☐	I,cI (yet)	8.	I talked to James about coming to the party _____
☐	☐	☐	I,cI (for)	9.	The football field was ruined _____
☐	☐	☐	I,cI (nor)	10.	Rich did not finish his classwork _____

COMPOUND SENTENCE LESSON 2B

Name _____

Date _____

INSTRUCTIONS:
1. Complete each of the following sentences to make a compound sentence by adding an independent clause. Match your sentence to the listed formula, and use the conjunction in parentheses if one is required. Be sure to include a comma or semicolon in each sentence.
2. Do the "S" Step of the "PENS" Strategy to the clause you have added to the sentence.
3. Mark each complete verb in your added clause with a "V."
4. Mark each main subject in your added clause with an "S."

EXAMPLE:		
I,cI (nor)	0.	We could not see the stars, nor could we see the moon.

			Formulas &	
M	**C**	**V&S**	**Conjunctions**	
☐	☐	☐	I,cI (and)	1. Scott rose at 5:00 A.M. to finish his paper _____
☐	☐	☐	I,cI (for)	2. James and Mary ignored Matt's warning _____
☐	☐	☐	I,cI (or)	3. You must go now _____
☐	☐	☐	I,cI (but)	4. The doctor did his best _____
☐	☐	☐	I,cI (so)	5. The food was rotten _____
☐	☐	☐	I;I	6. The football team would not give up _____
☐	☐	☐	I,cI (nor)	7. The baby did not cry _____
☐	☐	☐	I;I	8. The river was rising _____
☐	☐	☐	I,cI (yet)	9. Mike had just lost his job _____
☐	☐	☐	I;I	10. The space capsule landed on target _____

28

COMPOUND SENTENCE LESSON 2C

Name_____

Date_____

INSTRUCTIONS:
1. **Complete each of the following sentences to make a compound sentence by adding an independent clause. Match your sentence to the listed formula, and use the conjunction in parentheses if one is required. Be sure to include a comma or semicolon in each sentence.**
2. **Do the "S" Step of the "PENS" Strategy to the clause you have added to the sentence.**
3. **Mark each complete verb in your added clause with a "V."**
4. **Mark each main subject in your added clause with an "S."**

EXAMPLE:

I,cI   0.   We could not see the stars, _nor could we see the moon._

(nor)

M	C	V&S	Formulas & Conjunctions		
☐	☐	☐	I,cI (but)	1.	He started to go to the show _____
☐	☐	☐	I;I	2.	The ocean looked angry _____
☐	☐	☐	I,cI (for)	3.	Dan could not take the boys to the laboratory _____
☐	☐	☐	I,cI (and)	4.	Cody was winning _____
☐	☐	☐	I,cI (or)	5.	The project must be finished tonight _____
☐	☐	☐	I,cI (nor)	6.	The Governor will not meet with us _____
☐	☐	☐	I,cI (yet)	7.	We looked for a long time _____
☐	☐	☐	I;I	8.	Chris and Carrie wanted to wait at the bus station _____
☐	☐	☐	I,cI (so)	9.	The store will be closed tomorrow _____
☐	☐	☐	I;I	10.	The telephone rang _____

COMPOUND SENTENCE LESSON 2D

Name_____

Date_____

INSTRUCTIONS:

1. Complete each of the following sentences to make a compound sentence by adding an independent clause. Match your sentence to the listed formula, and use the conjunction in parentheses if one is required. Be sure to include a comma or semicolon in each sentence.
2. Do the "S" Step of the "PENS" Strategy to the clause you have added to the sentence.
3. Mark each complete verb in your added clause with a "V."
4. Mark each main subject in your added clause with an "S."

EXAMPLE:

I,cI   0.   We could not see the stars, _nor could we see the moon._
(nor)

M	C	V&S	Formulas & Conjunctions		
☐	☐	☐	I,cI (and)	1.	A group of hunters went to Africa _____
☐	☐	☐	I,cI (for)	2.	The stadium was filled to capacity _____
☐	☐	☐	I;I	3.	Hard work and extra effort are needed _____
☐	☐	☐	I,cI (nor)	4.	Jesse did not want to play _____
☐	☐	☐	I,cI (so)	5.	I have enough money for a stereo _____
☐	☐	☐	I;I	6.	The car cost $1000 to repair _____
☐	☐	☐	I,cI (or)	7.	You should give me that book _____
☐	☐	☐	I,cI (but)	8.	Kathy gets her new car on Friday _____
☐	☐	☐	I,cI (yet)	9.	The horse seemed fit _____
☐	☐	☐	I;I	10.	The President asked for organ donors _____

COMPOUND SENTENCE LESSON 3A

Name_____

Date_____

INSTRUCTIONS:

1. **For the first eight sentences, use the "PENS" Steps to write compound sentences to match the listed formulas. Use the conjunction in parentheses if one is required. Remember to punctuate each sentence correctly.**
2. **For the last two sentences, choose a formula for a compound sentence from your Formula Card. Write the formula on the blank to the left of the sentence. Use the "PENS" Steps to write a sentence that matches the formula you have chosen.**
3. **Be sure to check each sentence using the "S" Step of the "PENS" Strategy.**

EXAMPLE: **I,cI** 0. **(and)**	$\overset{S}{\text{The}}$ checkered flag $\overset{V}{\text{was lowered}}$, and the $\overset{S}{\text{crowd}}$ $\overset{V}{\text{roared}}$.

M   C   **Formulas & Conjunctions**

☐ ☐   I,cI (for)   1. _____

☐ ☐   I,cI (but)   2. _____

☐ ☐   I;I   3. _____

☐ ☐   I,cI (and)   4. _____

☐ ☐   I,cI (so)   5. _____

☐ ☐   I,cI (yet)   6. _____

☐ ☐   I,cI (or)   7. _____

☐ ☐   I;I   8. _____

☐ ☐   ____   9. _____

☐ ☐   ____   10. _____

31

COMPOUND SENTENCE LESSON 3B

Name_____

Date_____

INSTRUCTIONS:
1. **For the first eight sentences, use the "PENS" Steps to write compound sentences to match the listed formulas. Use the conjunction in parentheses if one is required. Remember to punctuate each sentence correctly.**
2. **For the last two sentences, choose a formula for a compound sentence from your Formula Card. Write the formula on the blank to the left of the sentence. Use the "PENS" Steps to write a sentence that matches the formula you have chosen.**
3. **Be sure to check each sentence using the "S" Step of the "PENS" Strategy.**

EXAMPLE: **I,cI** **(and)**	0. The checkered flag was lowered, and the crowd roared.

M	C	Formulas & Conjunctions	
☐	☐	I,cI (yet)	1. _____
☐	☐	I,cI (nor)	2. _____
☐	☐	I;I	3. _____
☐	☐	I,cI (but)	4. _____
☐	☐	I;I	5. _____
☐	☐	I,cI (for)	6. _____
☐	☐	I,cI (and)	7. _____
☐	☐	I,cI (so)	8. _____
☐	☐	____	9. _____
☐	☐	____	10. _____

COMPOUND SENTENCE LESSON 3C

Name_____

Date_____

INSTRUCTIONS:
1. For the first eight sentences, use the "PENS" Steps to write compound sentences to match the listed formulas. Use the conjunction in parentheses if one is required. Remember to punctuate each sentence correctly.
2. For the last two sentences, choose a formula for a compound sentence from your Formula Card. Write the formula on the blank to the left of the sentence. Use the "PENS" Steps to write a sentence that matches the formula you have chosen.
3. Be sure to check each sentence using the "S" Step of the "PENS" Strategy.

EXAMPLE:		
I,cI	0.	$\overset{S}{\text{The checkered}}$ $\overset{V}{\text{flag was lowered}}$, and the $\overset{S}{\text{crowd}}$ $\overset{V}{\text{roared}}$.
(and)		

M   C   **Formulas & Conjunctions**

☐ ☐   I,cI (nor)   1. _____

☐ ☐   I,cI (so)   2. _____

☐ ☐   I;I   3. _____

☐ ☐   I,cI (and)   4. _____

☐ ☐   I;I   5. _____

☐ ☐   I,cI (yet)   6. _____

☐ ☐   I,cI (for)   7. _____

☐ ☐   I,cI (or)   8. _____

☐ ☐   _____   9. _____

☐ ☐   _____   10. _____

COMPOUND SENTENCE LESSON 3D

Name_____

Date_____

INSTRUCTIONS:
1. **For the first eight sentences, use the "PENS" Steps to write compound sentences to match the listed formulas. Use the conjunction in parentheses if one is required. Remember to punctuate each sentence correctly.**
2. **For the last two sentences, choose a formula for a compound sentence from your Formula Card. Write the formula on the blank to the left of the sentence. Use the "PENS" Steps to write a sentence that matches the formula you have chosen.**
3. **Be sure to check each sentence using the "S" Step of the "PENS" Strategy.**

EXAMPLE:		
I,cI	0.	The checkered flag $\overset{S}{was}$ $\overset{V}{lowered}$, and the $\overset{S}{crowd}$ $\overset{V}{roared}$.
(and)		_____

M	C	Formulas & Conjunctions		
☐	☐	I,cI (and)	1.	_____
☐	☐	I,cI (but)	2.	_____
☐	☐	I,cI (for)	3.	_____
☐	☐	I,cI (or)	4.	_____
☐	☐	I;I	5.	_____
☐	☐	I,cI (yet)	6.	_____
☐	☐	I,cI (nor)	7.	_____
☐	☐	I;I	8.	_____
☐	☐	____	9.	_____
☐	☐	____	10.	_____

34

COMPOUND SENTENCE LESSON 4A

Name_____

Date_____

INSTRUCTIONS:
1. Do the "S" Step of the "PENS" Strategy for each sentence.
2. Mark each complete verb in each sentence with a "V."
3. Mark each main subject in each sentence with an "S."
4. In the blank to the left of the sentence, write the correct sentence formula for the sentence. Use your Formula Card to choose the correct formula.

EXAMPLE:

SSVV 0. The baseball team and football team got together and celebrated.

F   V   S   Formulas

☐ ☐ ☐   _____   1. Rick and James met at the arcade.

☐ ☐ ☐   _____   2. The guys went to the gym and lifted weights.

☐ ☐ ☐   _____   3. Randy rode many of the rides at the fair; Jeff tried only one.

☐ ☐ ☐   _____   4. Linda jumped and knocked the ball over the net.

☐ ☐ ☐   _____   5. John's serve looked good, but the judge called it out.

☐ ☐ ☐   _____   6. He stayed calm and served the ball again.

☐ ☐ ☐   _____   7. The Chiefs and Oilers both played on Sunday and won their games.

☐ ☐ ☐   _____   8. Ron has less than 2 months to live; cancer has spread throughout his body.

☐ ☐ ☐   _____   9. Over at the pool, Sue was swimming laps.

☐ ☐ ☐   _____   10. Linda wanted her to stop, but she refused.

COMPOUND SENTENCE LESSON 4B

Name_____

Date_____

INSTRUCTIONS:
1. **Do the "S" Step of the "PENS" Strategy for each sentence.**
2. **Mark each complete verb in each sentence with a "V."**
3. **Mark each main subject in each sentence with an "S."**
4. **In the blank to the left of the sentence, write the correct sentence formula for the sentence. Use your Formula Card to choose the correct formula.**

EXAMPLE:

                  S   S V   V

<u>SSVV</u> 0. The baseball team and football team got together and celebrated.

F   V   S   Formulas

☐ ☐ ☐ _____   1. Rick finished one job and started another.

☐ ☐ ☐ _____   2. Chip's hobby is old cars; I do not have a hobby.

☐ ☐ ☐ _____   3. Jenna laughed and glanced at the others.

☐ ☐ ☐ _____   4. Lindsay and Michael went out for dinner and saw a show.

☐ ☐ ☐ _____   5. The jury did not believe his story; they found him guilty.

☐ ☐ ☐ _____   6. Scott had to work at the concession stand, but he wanted to see the game.

☐ ☐ ☐ _____   7. James offered to help him on Saturday.

☐ ☐ ☐ _____   8. The police arrived quickly, and the burglar was caught.

☐ ☐ ☐ _____   9. They questioned him and searched his car.

☐ ☐ ☐ _____   10. Very late that night, the four men went home.

COMPOUND SENTENCE LESSON 4C

Name _____

Date _____

INSTRUCTIONS:
1. Do the "S" Step of the "PENS" Strategy for each sentence.
2. Mark each complete verb in each sentence with a "V."
3. Mark each main subject in each sentence with an "S."
4. In the blank to the left of the sentence, write the correct sentence formula for the sentence. Use your Formula Card to choose the correct formula.

EXAMPLE:

<u>SSVV</u> 0. The baseball team and football team got together and celebrated.

(marked: S over baseball team, S over football team, V over got, V over celebrated)

F   V   S   Formulas

☐ ☐ ☐ _____ 1. A mailman ran down the street and delivered the mail.

☐ ☐ ☐ _____ 2. A brown dog took a chunk out of the mailman's leg; the mailman yelled at the top of his lungs.

☐ ☐ ☐ _____ 3. He jumped through the bushes and over the flower bed.

☐ ☐ ☐ _____ 4. The boys and girls in the neighborhood watched with frightened eyes and whispered among themselves.

☐ ☐ ☐ _____ 5. The youngest boy ran to get his mother; the oldest boy called the police.

☐ ☐ ☐ _____ 6. The police arrived, and they asked lots of questions.

☐ ☐ ☐ _____ 7. The dog belongs to Mr. Perkins, but he will not feed the dog.

☐ ☐ ☐ _____ 8. Mr. Perkins and his wife live in the brown house on the corner.

☐ ☐ ☐ _____ 9. The brown house needs paint, but the Perkins family is too poor to buy the paint.

☐ ☐ ☐ _____ 10. The police captured the dog, and they put him in their van to be taken to the pound.

COMPOUND SENTENCE LESSON 4D

Name_____

Date_____

INSTRUCTIONS:
1. Do the "S" Step of the "PENS" Strategy for each sentence.
2. Mark each complete verb in each sentence with a "V."
3. Mark each main subject in each sentence with an "S."
4. In the blank to the left of the sentence, write the correct sentence formula for the sentence. Use your Formula Card to choose the correct formula.

EXAMPLE:

                   S   S   V   V

<u>SSVV</u> 0. The baseball team and football team got together and celebrated.

F   V   S   Formulas

☐ ☐ ☐ _____   1. Peter and his friends went on a picnic.

☐ ☐ ☐ _____   2. Peter was assigned to carry the picnic baskets, but he lost them.

☐ ☐ ☐ _____   3. He searched through the bushes and inspected the river bank.

☐ ☐ ☐ _____   4. The group had planned to eat fried chicken.

☐ ☐ ☐ _____   5. Peter was upset; he sat on a rock and thought.

☐ ☐ ☐ _____   6. His older brother and the others scolded him and told him to look in the bushes.

☐ ☐ ☐ _____   7. Peter found the picnic basket in the middle of a meadow, so he shouted for joy.

☐ ☐ ☐ _____   8. The boys sat in a circle; they passed the food around.

☐ ☐ ☐ _____   9. The chicken was "finger-licking good."

☐ ☐ ☐ _____   10. The picnic was a success, and the stomachs of all concerned were full.

COMPOUND SENTENCE LESSON 5A, 5B, 5C, 5D (circle one)

Name_____

Date_____

INSTRUCTIONS:
1. For the first eight items, use the "PENS" Steps to write a sentence that matches the listed formula. Use the conjunction in parentheses if one is required.
2. For the last two items, choose a formula, write the formula on the blank, and use the "PENS" Steps to write a sentence that matches the formula.
3. Be sure to use the "S" Step of the "PENS" Strategy to check whether each sentence matches the formula.

EXAMPLE: I;I	0.	The cake was beautiful; it was covered with lots of tiny flowers.

M	C	Formulas & Conjunctions	
☐	☐	S V	1. _____
☐	☐	I;I	2. _____
☐	☐	SS V	3. _____
☐	☐	I,cI (and)	4. _____
☐	☐	I,cI (but)	5. _____
☐	☐	S VV	6. _____
☐	☐	I,cI (so)	7. _____
☐	☐	SS VV	8. _____
☐	☐	Simple:	9. _____
☐	☐	Compound:	10. _____

COMPOUND SENTENCE LESSON 6A, 6B, 6C, 6D (circle one)

Name_____

Date_____

INSTRUCTIONS:
1. **In the space below, write at least six sentences about the topic listed on your Assignment Sheet. Include in this group of sentences at least two different kinds of simple sentences and two compound sentences. Use your Formula Card for reference as needed.**
2. **Use the "S" Step of the "PENS" Strategy and a *Compound Sentence Checklist* to check the kinds of sentences you have written.**
3. **Attach your completed *Compound Sentence Checklist* to this sheet when you are done.**

Topic: _____

_____

_____

_____

_____

_____

_____

_____

_____

_____

_____

_____

_____

_____

_____

_____

_____

_____

_____

_____

_____

COMPLEX SENTENCES

QUIZ AND LESSONS

COMPLEX SENTENCE QUIZ

Name_____

Date_____

- **You have learned about three types of sentences.**

  ☐ 1. <u>Simple sentences</u> have _____ independent clause(s).
  (How many?)

  ☐ 2. <u>Compound sentences</u> have _____ or more independent clauses.
  (How many?)

- **<u>Complex sentences</u> have:**

  ☐ 3. _____ independent clause(s) and
  (How many?)

  ☐ 4. _____ or more dependent clause(s).
  (How many?)

- **You have learned about two types of clauses:**

  ☐ 5. _____ clauses can stand alone.

  ☐ 6. _____ clauses cannot stand alone.

- **Many sentences have clauses that cannot stand alone.**

  Example Sentence #1: Kathy stayed home because she had a fever.

  ☐ 7. The clause that cannot stand alone in Example Sentence #1 is

  _____.

  Example Sentence #2: If the weather is nice, Sally likes to jog.

  ☐ 8. The clause that cannot stand alone in Example Sentence #2 is

  _____.

- **Remember that a <u>clause</u> is any group of words having a <u>subject</u> and a <u>verb</u>.**

  ☐ 9. Therefore, even a dependent clause has a _____

  and a _____ .

COMPLEX SENTENCE QUIZ (Continued)

Name_____

Example Sentence #3: I will sleep until the alarm rings.

☐ 10. The dependent clause in Example Sentence #3 is _____

_____ .

☐ 11. The verb in the dependent clause in Example Sentence #3 is _____ .

☐ 12. The main subject of the dependent clause in Example Sentence #3 is

_____ .

● **Do not confuse an introductory group of words in a sentence like the one in Example Sentence #4 for a dependent clause.**

Example Sentence #4: While running quickly, Paul got a cramp.

☐ 13. The first group of words in Example Sentence #4 is not a dependent clause because

it does not have a _____ .

● **A dependent clause normally starts with a word that shows its relationship to the independent clause. These words are called <u>subordinating conjunctions.</u>**

<u>If,</u> <u>because,</u> <u>although,</u> and <u>unless</u> are examples of subordinating conjunctions.

Example Sentence #5: I love to cook although it takes time.

☐ 14. The subordinating conjunction in Example Sentence #5 is _____ .

Example Sentence #6: The girls won't come unless you call them.

☐
☐ 15. In Example Sentence #6, <u>unless</u> is the _____

_____ .

☐
☐ 16. In Example Sentence #6, <u>unless</u> shows the relationship between

the _____ clause and the

_____ clause.

COMPLEX SENTENCE QUIZ (Continued)

Example Sentence #7: The turkey is not thawed because we forgot to take it out of the freezer.

☐ 17. The subordinating conjunction in Example Sentence #7 is _____ .

☐ 18. The subordinating conjunction shows the _____ between the dependent clause and the independent clause.

● **Remember, a complex sentence has one independent clause and at least one dependent clause.**

In the following sentences, underline the <u>independent clause</u> with two lines and the <u>dependent clause</u> with one line.

☐ 19. I will go to the store after I make a shopping list.

☐ 20. When he eats his food, the dog gets meat all over his face.

☐ 21. Since she is my closest friend, I will buy something special for her birthday.

● **If the dependent clause comes <u>before</u> the independent clause, use a comma to separate the two clauses. (D,I)**

No comma is needed if the dependent clause comes <u>after</u> the independent clause. (ID)

Put commas where they are required in the sentences below. If a sentence does not need a comma, leave it as it is.

☐ 22. My dad will be happy if I get good grades this semester.

☐ 23. Since Jason is a good student he will probably get all As.

☐ 24. I never would have believed it if I had not seen it.

☐ 25. When you have decided please let me know.

☐ 26. The car was fine before I had the wreck.

☐ 27. After they went skating the guys went out for a pizza.

☐ 28. Once the work was done the four teenagers went for a ride.

COMPLEX SENTENCE LESSON 1A

Name_____

Date_____

INSTRUCTIONS:
For the following complex sentences:
1. **Underline the <u>independent clause</u> with two lines.**
2. **Underline the <u>dependent clause</u> with one line.**
3. **In the blank to the left of the sentence, write the correct formula for the sentence. Use your Formula Card to choose the correct formula.**

EXAMPLE:

<u>ID</u>   0. <u>The sirens wailed</u> until all danger had passed.

F   L   Formulas

☐ ☐   _____   1. I will rake the leaves myself unless you want to join me.

☐ ☐   _____   2. After the fans went home, the band packed up their instruments.

☐ ☐   _____   3. Until Jill learns how to pace herself, she will not be healthy.

☐ ☐   _____   4. That car is perfect for me because I can afford its upkeep.

☐ ☐   _____   5. Since the weather got warm, we have been driving with the top down.

☐ ☐   _____   6. Whenever Hanni smiles at me, my heart melts.

☐ ☐   _____   7. Will you wait for me while I speak to Mr. Low?

☐ ☐   _____   8. Before you buy a boa constrictor, you should think about future problems.

☐ ☐   9. Although she was scared to death, Kathy gave a short speech to the class.
        _____

☐ ☐   10. I will buy a home even if I have to save for ten years.
        _____

COMPLEX SENTENCE LESSON 1B

Name_____

Date_____

INSTRUCTIONS:
For the following complex sentences:
1. Underline the <u>independent clause</u> with two lines.
2. Underline the <u>dependent clause</u> with one line.
3. In the blank to the left of the sentence, write the correct formula for the sentence. Use your Formula Card to choose the correct formula.

EXAMPLE:

<u>I D</u>   0.   <u>The sirens wailed</u> until all danger had passed.

F   L   **Formulas**

☐ ☐   _____   1.   While snow was falling, the streets were silent.

☐ ☐   _____   2.   After we finish this homework, we should call Joe and go to the dance.

☐ ☐   _____   3.   The repairman will come tomorrow if he can find the time.

☐ ☐   _____   4.   Because the thief was noisy, he was caught opening the safe.

☐ ☐   _____   5.   Shanna looked happy once her test was over.

☐ ☐   _____   6.   Until Jake learns to study, he will continue to fail.

☐ ☐   _____   7.   Candy wore a floppy hat as if she wanted to hide her face.

☐ ☐   _____   8.   Whenever you see our lights on, we are at home.

☐ ☐   _____   9.   Although we were careful, we still got lost.

☐ ☐   _____   10.   Even if we have the best team, we may not win.

COMPLEX SENTENCE LESSON 1C

Name_____

Date_____

INSTRUCTIONS:
For the following complex sentences:
1. **Underline the <u>independent clause</u> with two lines.**
2. **Underline the <u>dependent clause</u> with one line.**
3. **In the blank to the left of the sentence, write the correct formula for the sentence. Use your Formula Card to choose the correct formula.**

EXAMPLE:

<u>ID</u>   0. <u>The sirens wailed</u> until all danger had passed.

F   L   Formulas

☐ ☐ _____   1. Unless the rain stops soon, we will have to postpone the picnic.

☐ ☐ _____   2. Whenever the birds fly south, winter is on the way.

☐ ☐ _____   3. Sara quit the basketball team although she had been one of the starting five.

☐ ☐ _____   4. If Don is ready on time, he can go to the concert with us.

☐ ☐ _____   5. Even if I am nominated, I will not run for class president.

☐ ☐ _____   6. Carrie acts as if she does not care about anything or anybody.

☐ ☐ _____   7. The sky looks as though we might get some snow.

☐ ☐ _____   8. Wherever there is smoke, there is a fire.

☐ ☐ _____   9. Even though our team came in second, we felt like champions.

☐ ☐ _____   10. Jerry would prefer doing the extra assignment so that he will not have to study tonight.

COMPLEX SENTENCE LESSON 1D

Name_____

Date_____

INSTRUCTIONS:
For the following complex sentences:
1. **Underline the <u>independent clause</u> with two lines.**
2. **Underline the <u>dependent clause</u> with one line.**
3. **In the blank to the left of the sentence, write the correct formula for the sentence. Use your Formula Card to choose the correct formula.**

EXAMPLE:

<u>I D</u>   0. <u><u>The sirens wailed</u></u> <u>until all danger had passed.</u>

F   L   Formulas

☐ ☐ _____ 1. If the students agree on a guest speaker, the school will pay the travel expenses.

☐ ☐ _____ 2. Chris wants to try out for the soccer team since he has been playing for years.

☐ ☐ _____ 3. Mr. Jones made the assignment twice as long because everyone had failed to hand in the first one.

☐ ☐ _____ 4. After Darla finishes practicing, we can go to the movies.

☐ ☐ _____ 5. Tim cleaned the house before his parents returned on Sunday.

☐ ☐ _____ 6. While Marilyn and Debbie were in Florida, they got great tans.

☐ ☐ _____ 7. Until Scott learns the rules of the game, winning will be difficult.

☐ ☐ _____ 8. The candidate stopped talking when the moderator gave him the signal.

☐ ☐ _____ 9. Once the band members know the costs, they can make their plans for the trip.

☐ ☐ _____ 10. Pete's parents will let him drive the car if he pays for the gas.

COMPLEX SENTENCE LESSON 2A

Name_____

Date_____

INSTRUCTIONS:
1. **Make each of the following into a complex sentence that matches the listed formula. Use the listed subordinating conjunction if one is needed. Be sure to include a comma if one is needed.**
2. **Do the "S" Step of the "PENS" Strategy on each clause that you have added.**
3. **Mark each complete verb in each added clause with a "V."**
4. **Mark each main subject in each added clause with an "S."**

EXAMPLE:
ID   0. Sarah started crying _____when she heard the bad news_____
(when)   _about her grandfather._

    (with handwritten S and V marks: S over "she", V over "heard")

M	C	V&S	Formulas & Conjunctions
☐	☐	☐	ID (because) 1. I want to earn some money _____
☐	☐	☐	D,I 2. Unless he gets some help _____
☐	☐	☐	D,I 3. When Paulette arrives _____
☐	☐	☐	ID (so that) 4. Jan came early _____
☐	☐	☐	D,I 5. Since I have been going to the doctor _____
☐	☐	☐	ID (after) 6. He will go swimming _____
☐	☐	☐	ID (although) 7. The car is ready _____
☐	☐	☐	D,I 8. Until we finish the work _____
☐	☐	☐	ID (if) 9. The builder will start the house _____
☐	☐	☐	D,I 10. Before James leaves _____

COMPLEX SENTENCE LESSON 2B

Name_____

Date_____

INSTRUCTIONS:
1. **Make each of the following into a complex sentence that matches the listed formula. Use the listed subordinating conjunction if one is needed. Be sure to include a comma if one is needed.**
2. **Do the "S" Step of the "PENS" Strategy on each clause that you have added.**
3. **Mark each complete verb in each added clause with a "V."**
4. **Mark each main subject in each added clause with an "S."**

EXAMPLE:	
ID	0. Sarah started crying <u>when</u> <u>she heard the bad news</u>
(when)	<u>about her grandfather.</u>

In the example, handwritten: when she heard the bad news about her grandfather. With "S" above "she" and "V" above "heard".

M	C	S&V	**Formulas & Conjunctions**
☐	☐	☐	ID 1. Matt talked to him _____ (while) _____
☐	☐	☐	ID 2. Jean will go _____ (whenever) _____
☐	☐	☐	D,I 3. Because today is Thursday _____
☐	☐	☐	ID 4. Jan will give you the money _____ (when) _____
☐	☐	☐	D,I 5. Unless we find the basketball _____
☐	☐	☐	D,I 6. In order that she would be on time _____
☐	☐	☐	ID 7. Jesse has not slept well _____ (since) _____
☐	☐	☐	D,I 8. Whenever this game ends _____
☐	☐	☐	ID 9. Jenna cannot go jogging _____ (until) _____
☐	☐	☐	D,I 10. If you will call me tonight _____

51

COMPLEX SENTENCE LESSON 2C

Name_____

Date_____

INSTRUCTIONS:
1. Make each of the following into a complex sentence that matches the listed formula. Use the listed subordinating conjunction if one is needed. Be sure to include a comma if one is needed.
2. Do the "S" Step of the "PENS" Strategy on each clause that you have added.
3. Mark each complete verb in each added clause with a "V."
4. Mark each main subject in each added clause with an "S."

EXAMPLE:

ID 0. Sarah started crying _____S____V____ when she heard the bad news _____
(when) about her grandfather.

M	C	V&S	Formulas & Conjunctions	
☐	☐	☐	D,I	1. After the show was over _____
☐	☐	☐	ID (because)	2. She was unhappy _____
☐	☐	☐	ID (unless)	3. I do not want to go _____
☐	☐	☐	ID (provided)	4. The Dolphins will win the game _____
☐	☐	☐	D,I	5. Until I am sure _____
☐	☐	☐	D,I	6. Since I have started studying at home _____
☐	☐	☐	ID (even though)	7. I like my best friend _____
☐	☐	☐	D,I	8. When he sees this mess _____
☐	☐	☐	ID (before)	9. Steve will call you tonight _____
☐	☐	☐	D,I	10. As long as I have some money _____

COMPLEX SENTENCE LESSON 2D

Name_____

Date_____

INSTRUCTIONS:
1. Make each of the following into a complex sentence that matches the listed formula. Use the listed subordinating conjunction if one is needed. Be sure to include a comma if one is needed.
2. Do the "S" Step of the "PENS" Strategy on each clause that you have added.
3. Mark each complete verb in each added clause with a "V."
4. Mark each main subject in each added clause with an "S."

EXAMPLE:			
ID	0. Sarah started crying	S V	
(when)	_when she heard the bad news_		
	about her grandfather.		

M	C	V&S	**Formulas & Conjunctions**	
☐	☐	☐	ID (unless)	1. You should not jump _____
☐	☐	☐	D,I	2. Since we have some wood and a few matches _____
☐	☐	☐	ID (since)	3. I must take this book back to the library _____
☐	☐	☐	D,I	4. Until we can get some food _____
☐	☐	☐	ID (when)	5. She found out about the theft _____
☐	☐	☐	D,I	6. If the dog buries his bone _____
☐	☐	☐	D,I	7. As long as his things are hidden _____
☐	☐	☐	ID (just as)	8. The candle flickered _____
☐	☐	☐	D,I	9. Unless you give me the loot _____
☐	☐	☐	ID (although)	10. Paul loves to jog _____

COMPLEX SENTENCE LESSON 3A

Name_____

Date_____

INSTRUCTIONS:
1. Write a complex sentence that matches each of the listed formulas. Include the listed subordinating conjunction in your sentence.
2. For the last two sentences, choose your own formula and subordinating conjunction. Write the formula to the left of the sentence on the blank, and write a matching sentence.
3. Be sure to check your work using the "S" Step of the "PENS" Strategy on each sentence.

EXAMPLE:		
D,I (if)	0.	If you want me to take you, I will pick you up at ten o'clock.

M   C   **Formulas &
Conjunctions**

☐ ☐   D,I
(because)   1. _____

☐ ☐   D,I
(unless)   2. _____

☐ ☐   ID
(when)   3. _____

☐ ☐   D,I
(although)   4. _____

☐ ☐   ID
(if)   5. _____

☐ ☐   ID
(since)   6. _____

☐ ☐   D,I
(after)   7. _____

☐ ☐   ID
(until)   8. _____

☐ ☐   _____   9. _____

☐ ☐   _____   10. _____

COMPLEX SENTENCE LESSON 3B

Name_____

Date_____

INSTRUCTIONS:
1. **Write a complex sentence that matches each of the listed formulas. Include the listed subordinating conjunction in your sentence.**
2. **For the last two sentences, choose your own formula and subordinating conjunction. Write the formula to the left of the sentence on the blank, and write a matching sentence.**
3. **Be sure to check your work using the "S" Step of the "PENS" Strategy on each sentence.**

EXAMPLE:
D,I 0. _If you want me to take you, I will pick you up_
(if)   _at ten o'clock._

M C   **Formulas & Conjunctions**

☐ ☐   ID (before)   1. _____

☐ ☐   ID (as if)   2. _____

☐ ☐   D,I (as long as)   3. _____

☐ ☐   D,I (while)   4. _____

☐ ☐   ID (even if)   5. _____

☐ ☐   D,I (once)   6. _____

☐ ☐   ID (so that)   7. _____

☐ ☐   D,I (whenever)   8. _____

☐ ☐   _____   9. _____

☐ ☐   _____   10. _____

COMPLEX SENTENCE LESSON 3C

Name_____

Date_____

INSTRUCTIONS:
1. **Write a complex sentence that matches each of the listed formulas. Include the listed subordinating conjunction in your sentence.**
2. **For the last two sentences, choose your own formula and subordinating conjunction. Write the formula to the left of the sentence on the blank, and write a matching sentence.**
3. **Be sure to check your work using the "S" Step of the "PENS" Strategy on each sentence.**

EXAMPLE: **D,I** (**if**)	0. _If you want me to take you, I will pick you up at ten o'clock._

M   C

Formulas & Conjunctions

☐ ☐   ID
(in order that)   1._____

☐ ☐   D,I
(unless)   2._____

☐ ☐   D,I
(before)   3._____

☐ ☐   ID
(although)   4._____

☐ ☐   ID
(since)   5._____

☐ ☐   D,I
(when)   6._____

☐ ☐   ID
(even though)   7._____

☐ ☐   D,I
(after)   8._____

☐ ☐   _____
    9._____

☐ ☐   _____
    10._____

56

COMPLEX SENTENCE LESSON 3D

Name_____

Date_____

INSTRUCTIONS:
1. Write a complex sentence that matches each of the listed formulas. Include the listed subordinating conjunction in your sentence.
2. For the last two sentences, choose your own formula and subordinating conjunction. Write the formula to the left of the sentence on the blank, and write a matching sentence.
3. Be sure to check your work using the "S" Step of the "PENS" Strategy on each sentence.

EXAMPLE:	
D,I (if)	0. _If you want me to take you, I will pick you up at ten o'clock._

M	C	Formulas & Conjunctions	
☐	☐	D,I (even if)	1. _____
☐	☐	ID (so that)	2. _____
☐	☐	D,I (because)	3. _____
☐	☐	ID (while)	4. _____
☐	☐	D,I (until)	5. _____
☐	☐	ID (if)	6. _____
☐	☐	D,I (whenever)	7. _____
☐	☐	ID (once)	8. _____
☐	☐	_____	9. _____
☐	☐	_____	10. _____

COMPLEX SENTENCE LESSON 4A

Name_____

Date_____

INSTRUCTIONS:
1. **Underline each <u>independent clause</u> with two lines.**
2. **Underline each <u>dependent clause</u> with one line.**
3. **In the blank to the left of each sentence, write the correct sentence formula for the sentence. Use your Formula Card to choose the correct formula.**

EXAMPLE:

<u>ID</u>   0. <u>The plane had a perfect landing</u> <u>until the brakes failed</u>.

F   L   Formulas

☐ ☐ _____   1. Jess and Rick took the bus to the concert.

☐ ☐ _____   2. Everyone had a good time.

☐ ☐ _____   3. Unless you are willing to practice, you cannot learn to write.

☐ ☐ _____   4. The boss demanded a lot, and the people worked hard.

☐ ☐ _____   5. The car was painted a bright blue.

☐ ☐ _____   6. We went to get pizza, but we did not get to go to the show.

☐ ☐ _____   7. The managers were unable to reach an agreement because their differences were too great.

☐ ☐ _____   8. Joe's sister and brother went to the game with us; they enjoyed it.

☐ ☐ _____   9. I think I'd better stay home, yet your offer is very appealing.

☐ ☐ _____ 10. The nurse handed the scalpel to the doctor when she asked for it.

COMPLEX SENTENCE LESSON 4B

Name_____

Date_____

INSTRUCTIONS:
1. Underline each <u>independent clause</u> with two lines.
2. Underline each <u>dependent clause</u> with one line.
3. In the blank to the left of each sentence, write the correct sentence formula for the sentence. Use your Formula Card to choose the correct formula.

EXAMPLE:

<u>I D</u>   0. <u><u>The plane had a perfect landing</u></u> <u>until the brakes failed.</u>

F   L   **Formulas**

☐ ☐   _____   1.   We got up at 5:00 A.M., so we left early.

☐ ☐   _____   2.   Let's work now; we will play later.

☐ ☐   _____   3.   The trees should not be pruned until they have lost their leaves.

☐ ☐   _____   4.   Books and newspapers can be found in the library or study.

☐ ☐   _____   5.   Tim likes to ride motorcycles, but his girlfriend refuses to ride with him.

☐ ☐   _____   6.   This library had fewer than a thousand books before the alumni presented their gift.

☐ ☐   _____   7.   I grade a lot of quizzes and make up a lot of assignment sheets.

☐ ☐   _____   8.   Because he asked me, I will go.

☐ ☐   _____   9.   The peaches and plums smelled and tasted good.

☐ ☐   _____   10. You can stay here, or you can leave and go home.

COMPLEX SENTENCE LESSON 4C

Name_____

Date_____

INSTRUCTIONS:
1. Underline each <u>independent clause</u> with two lines.
2. Underline each <u>dependent clause</u> with one line.
3. In the blank to the left of each sentence, write the correct sentence formula for the sentence. Use your Formula Card to choose the correct formula.

EXAMPLE:

<u>ID</u>   0. <u>The plane had a perfect landing</u> until the brakes failed.

F   L   Formulas

☐ ☐ _____   1. If you will come over here, I will give you some information for your paper.

☐ ☐ _____   2. Jerry gave Mary his pen and took it away.

☐ ☐ _____   3. The ball flew up into the air, and Peter caught it.

☐ ☐ _____   4. Don't forget to pick me up because I do not want to miss the meeting.

☐ ☐ _____   5. Although Dean and Kari liked the party, they did not stay.

☐ ☐ _____   6. Sally and Bill ate popcorn, and it tasted delicious.

☐ ☐ _____   7. Dara called me and left a message, but I did not return the call.

☐ ☐ _____   8. The sandwiches and pop are here and are ready to be eaten.

☐ ☐ _____   9. After Reed thought about the problem, he found a solution.

☐ ☐ _____   10. Lila and Don ran and dived into the water.

COMPLEX SENTENCE LESSON 4D

Name_____

Date_____

INSTRUCTIONS:
1. **Underline each <u>independent clause</u> with two lines.**
2. **Underline each <u>dependent clause</u> with one line.**
3. **In the blank to the left of each sentence, write the correct sentence formula for the sentence. Use your Formula Card to choose the correct formula.**

EXAMPLE:

<u>I D</u>   0. The plane had a perfect landing until the brakes failed.

F	L	Formulas		
☐	☐	_____	1.	Dean will go to the fair if he finishes all of his chores.
☐	☐	_____	2.	We went swimming at the lake last Saturday.
☐	☐	_____	3.	Matt studied hard for his algebra test; he did not work hard on the science project.
☐	☐	_____	4.	It will be 9:30 before we can leave.
☐	☐	_____	5.	Running to the bus, David tripped and fell.
☐	☐	_____	6.	Kim and David stopped working and started something else.
☐	☐	_____	7.	If Scott goes, James will agree to go.
☐	☐	_____	8.	Kathy works hard at school.
☐	☐	_____	9.	Jerry wants to go, yet he has to stay and work.
☐	☐	_____	10.	After the sun came up, the boys went out into the field and worked.

COMPLEX SENTENCE LESSON 5A

Name_____

Date_____

INSTRUCTIONS:
1. **For the first six items, write a sentence that matches the listed formula. Use the conjunction in parentheses if one is required.**
2. **For the last four items, choose a formula, write the formula on the blank, and write a sentence that matches the formula.**
3. **Be sure to check your work by using the "S" Step of the "PENS" Strategy on each sentence.**

EXAMPLE:
D,I
(until)

0. _Until the tide goes out, swimmers should not go in the water._

		Formulas & Conjunctions	
M	**C**		
☐	☐	SS V	1. _____
			_____
☐	☐	ID (because)	2. _____
			_____
☐	☐	I,cI (but)	3. _____
			_____
☐	☐	D,I (although)	4. _____
			_____
☐	☐	S VV	5. _____
			_____
☐	☐	I;I	6. _____
			_____
☐	☐	Complex: _____	7. _____
☐	☐	Simple: _____	8. _____
☐	☐	Compound: _____	9. _____
☐	☐	Complex: _____	10. _____

COMPLEX SENTENCE LESSON 5B

Name_____

Date_____

INSTRUCTIONS:
1. For the first six items, write a sentence that matches the listed formula. Use the conjunction in parentheses if one is required.
2. For the last four items, choose a formula, write the formula on the blank, and write a sentence that matches the formula.
3. Be sure to check your work by using the "S" Step of the "PENS" Strategy on each sentence.

EXAMPLE:		
D,I (until)	0.	_Until the tide goes out, swimmers should not go in the water._

M	C	Formulas & Conjunctions	
☐	☐	D,I (until)	1. _____
☐	☐	I,cI (and)	2. _____
☐	☐	S VV	3. _____
☐	☐	I;I	4. _____
☐	☐	ID (if)	5. _____
☐	☐	SS VV	6. _____
☐	☐	Complex:	7. _____
☐	☐	Simple:	8. _____
☐	☐	Compound:	9. _____
☐	☐	Complex:	10. _____

COMPLEX SENTENCE LESSON 5C

Name_____

Date_____

INSTRUCTIONS:
1. For the first six items, write a sentence that matches the listed formula. Use the conjunction in parentheses if one is required.
2. For the last four items, choose a formula, write the formula on the blank, and write a sentence that matches the formula.
3. Be sure to check your work by using the "S" Step of the "PENS" Strategy on each sentence.

EXAMPLE:		
D,I	0.	_Until the tide goes out, swimmers should not go in the water._
(until)		

M   C   **Formulas & Conjunctions**

☐ ☐   D,I (before)   1. _____

☐ ☐   I,cI (yet)   2. _____

☐ ☐   S VV   3. _____

☐ ☐   I;I   4. _____

☐ ☐   ID (since)   5. _____

☐ ☐   SS V   6. _____

☐ ☐   Complex: 7. _____

☐ ☐   Simple: 8. _____

☐ ☐   Compound: 9. _____

☐ ☐   Complex: 10. _____

COMPLEX SENTENCE LESSON 5D

Name_____

Date_____

INSTRUCTIONS:
1. **For the first six items, write a sentence that matches the listed formula. Use the conjunction in parentheses if one is required.**
2. **For the last four items, choose a formula, write the formula on the blank, and write a sentence that matches the formula.**
3. **Be sure to check your work by using the "S" Step of the "PENS" Strategy on each sentence.**

EXAMPLE:	
D,I 0.	_Until the tide goes out, swimmers should not go_
(until)	_in the water._

M	C	Formulas & Conjunctions	
☐	☐	I,cI (or)	1. _____
☐	☐	S VV	2. _____
☐	☐	ID (after)	3. _____
☐	☐	I;I	4. _____
☐	☐	D,I (unless)	5. _____
☐	☐	SS VV	6. _____
☐	☐	Complex: _____	7. _____
☐	☐	Simple: _____	8. _____
☐	☐	Compound: _____	9. _____
☐	☐	Complex: _____	10. _____

COMPLEX SENTENCE LESSON 6A, 6B, 6C, 6D (circle one)

Name_____

Date_____

INSTRUCTIONS:
1. In the space below, use the "PENS" Strategy to write at least six sentences about the topic listed on your Assignment Sheet. Include in this group of sentences at least one compound sentence and two complex sentences.
2. Use the "S" Step of the "PENS" Strategy and a *Complex Sentence Checklist* to check the kinds of sentences you have written.
3. Attach your completed *Complex Sentence Checklist* to this sheet when you are done.

Topic: _____

_____

_____

_____

_____

_____

_____

_____

_____

_____

_____

_____

_____

_____

_____

_____

_____

_____

_____

_____

COMPOUND-COMPLEX SENTENCES

QUIZ AND LESSONS

COMPOUND-COMPLEX
SENTENCE QUIZ

Name_____

Date_____

INSTRUCTIONS: Read the information, and fill in the blanks.

● **You have learned about four types of sentences.**

☐ 1. Simple sentences have _____ independent clause(s).
(How many?)

☐ 2. Compound sentences have _____ or more independent clauses.
(How many?)

☐ 3. Complex sentences have _____ independent clause(s) and
(How many?)

☐ _____ or more dependent clauses.
(How many?)

☐ 4. Compound-complex sentences have _____ or more independent
(How many?)

☐ clauses and at least _____ dependent clause(s).
(How many?)

● **You have learned about two types of clauses.**

☐ 5. A(n) _____ clause is one that can stand alone.

☐ 6. A(n) _____ clause cannot stand alone.

● **In Example Sentence #1, the independent clauses are underlined with two lines, and the dependent clause is underlined with one line.**

Example Sentence #1:
When John needs to go home, he should tell me, and I will drive him there.

Underline the <u>independent clauses</u> twice and the <u>dependent clauses</u> once in the following sentences:

☐☐☐ 7. When they were late, the boss got angry, and they had to work overtime.

☐☐☐ 8. The girls stayed out until the moon had risen, so they got in trouble with their parents.

☐☐☐ 9. Anna scraped, and Tony sanded while I went to buy some paint.

- **You must pay careful attention to punctuate compound-complex sentences correctly.**

  ☐ 10. The type of punctuation that is used between two independent clauses that are joined with a coordinating conjunction is the _____ .

  ☐ 11. The other type of punctuation that is used between two independent clauses is the _____ .

  ☐ 12. The type of punctuation used between a dependent clause and an independent clause when the dependent clause is <u>first</u> is the _____ .

Punctuate these sentences correctly by following the rules you have learned about punctuating compound-complex sentences:

☐ ☐ 13. Unless you can prove your innocence we will have to try you and perhaps we will convict you.

☐ 14. We will not know the winner for sure until the meet is over so you will just have to wait and see.

☐ ☐ 15. Because they are both very good sometimes Jean wins first place and sometimes Susie wins first place.

☐ ☐ 16. Before Kathy went she made potato salad and she packed the picnic basket.

☐ 17. Mike moved away but he continues to be our friend even though we rarely see him.

☐ ☐ 18. Whenever we need help we call Pete he will drop everything to help us.

COMPOUND-COMPLEX SENTENCE
LESSON 1A

Name_____

Date_____

INSTRUCTIONS:
For each of the following compound-complex sentences:
1. Underline the <u>independent clauses</u> with two lines.
2. Underline the <u>dependent clause</u> with one line.
3. In the blank to the left of the sentence, write the correct sentence formula. Use your Formula Card to choose the correct formula.

EXAMPLE:

<u>D,I;I</u>   0. Unless we get rain, I would like to go boating; I have not gone for two weeks.

F   L   Formulas

☐ ☐   _____   1. She should come soon, but I will not be disappointed if she does not arrive.

☐ ☐   _____   2. When he has time, Tom will write his paper; he will also do his math.

☐ ☐   _____   3. Janice must stay home; she has to babysit until her parents come back.

☐ ☐   _____   4. Jeff will leave when Rick does, and Scott will leave later.

☐ ☐   _____   5. After the boys waited for hours, the girls finally came, and they all went out for pizza.

☐ ☐   _____   6. The builders worked until the rain began; they huddled together in the hut.

☐ ☐   _____   7. Since Jan and Jen are done, they can go get Jim, and we can all go to the show.

☐ ☐   _____   8. Hitler retained power until he died, and his reign lasted ten years.

☐ ☐   _____   9. Unless he returns soon, we will have to leave; we should not be late for the play.

☐ ☐   _____   10. I would like to go because I really like to shop, but I have to finish this project first.

COMPOUND-COMPLEX SENTENCE
LESSON 1B

Name_____

Date_____

INSTRUCTIONS:
For each of the following compound-complex sentences:
1. Underline the <u>independent clauses</u> with two lines.
2. Underline the <u>dependent clause</u> with one line.
3. In the blank to the left of the sentence, write the correct sentence formula. Use your Formula Card to choose the correct formula.

EXAMPLE:

<u>D,I; I</u> 0. <u>Unless we get rain</u>, <u>I would like to go boating</u>; <u>I have not gone for two weeks</u>.

F   L   Formulas

☐ ☐ _____ 1. Before they left, George had eaten all the pizza, and Sam had drunk all the pop.

☐ ☐ _____ 2. The peace treaty was finally signed; six weeks passed before the agreement was reached.

☐ ☐ _____ 3. I will go early, so we will be sure to get tickets although the show may already be sold out.

☐ ☐ _____ 4. When he was on his way downtown, Sam had a wreck, and the ambulance took him to the hospital.

☐ ☐ _____ 5. Keith visited Kim after he left work; he had no other free time.

☐ ☐ _____ 6. Linda read the book since it was the required assignment, but she did not understand it.

☐ ☐ _____ 7. Unless you can do better in your work, we will have to fire you; we can hire a replacement.

☐ ☐ _____ 8. When she asked about the dog, no one replied; they all stared at the floor.

☐ ☐ _____ 9. I worked hard, and George worked even harder until the job was done.

☐ ☐ _____ 10. Because the University had budget cuts, many of the telephones were removed, and the heat was turned down.

COMPOUND-COMPLEX SENTENCE
LESSON 1C

Name_____

Date_____

INSTRUCTIONS:
For each of the following compound-complex sentences:
1. Underline the <u>independent clauses</u> with two lines.
2. Underline the <u>dependent clause</u> with one line.
3. In the blank to the left of the sentence, write the correct sentence formula. Use your Formula Card to choose the correct formula.

EXAMPLE:

<u>D,I;I</u> 0. <u>Unless we get rain</u>, <u><u>I would like to go boating</u></u>; <u><u>I have not gone for two weeks</u></u>.

F   L   Formulas

☐ ☐ _____   1. The chef made a great meal, and we all enjoyed it although we overate.

☐ ☐ _____   2. The repairs on my car should cost hundreds of dollars; I will have to sell it unless you can help me fix it cheaply.

☐ ☐ _____   3. If nuclear war breaks out, animal life will probably not survive; plant life will not exist either.

☐ ☐ _____   4. Because the storm has begun, there is no one outside, and all of the shutters on the houses are closed.

☐ ☐ _____   5. I wanted to go before he got here, but he came early.

☐ ☐ _____   6. Before Dean could try out for the football team, his parents had to sign a permission slip, and he had to take a physical examination.

☐ ☐ _____   7. Alvamar Golf Course is a "tournament" quality course; it has the facilities necessary to hold a major golf tournament although none has been held there yet.

☐ ☐ _____   8. If Jeff does not come soon, we will not have time to get to the store, nor will Ann get a chance to meet him.

☐ ☐ _____   9. Mary should not drive to Kansas City tonight since the storm is so fierce; she can spend the night at my house.

☐ ☐ _____   10. Kevin had collected a lot of camping gear, and he had all the menus planned although he could not go camping for two weeks.

COMPOUND-COMPLEX SENTENCE
LESSON 1D

Name_____

Date_____

INSTRUCTIONS:
For each of the following compound-complex sentences:
1. Underline the <u>independent clauses</u> with two lines.
2. Underline the <u>dependent clause</u> with one line.
3. In the blank to the left of the sentence, write the correct sentence formula. Use your Formula Card to choose the correct formula.

EXAMPLE:

D,I;I   0. <u>Unless we get rain,</u> <u>I would like to go boating;</u> <u>I have not gone for two weeks.</u>

F   L   Formulas

☐ ☐ _____ 1. The theatre was crowded before the concert began; everyone had wanted to get good seats.

☐ ☐ _____ 2. Although together they had enough to buy the car, Jan does not have enough money; Jean does not have much either.

☐ ☐ _____ 3. There has been a lot of concern about the use of nuclear weapons because many countries have developed them, but there have been no agreements made.

☐ ☐ _____ 4. The President proposed the legislation, and Congress passed it before anyone had a chance to object.

☐ ☐ _____ 5. Because John was late, the whole group missed the show, and everyone was upset.

☐ ☐ _____ 6. The other way of dealing with the problem is to ignore it, yet this is not good since you often are caught unprepared in an emergency.

☐ ☐ _____ 7. The Surgeon General has stated the dangers of smoking; this seems to have had little effect on cigarette sales because people ignore the warning.

☐ ☐ _____ 8. Gene wanted to buy the house; I wanted to buy it too after I found out the price.

☐ ☐ _____ 9. Since Debbie had fifteen books to return to the library, Karl drove her, so she could take them all back.

☐ ☐ _____ 10. Unless the baseball team finds a sponsor, we will not be able to play in the league; our chances of winning the championship look dim.

COMPOUND-COMPLEX SENTENCE
LESSON 2A

Name_____

Date_____

INSTRUCTIONS:
1. Complete each of the following sentences to make a compound-complex sentence. Match your sentence to the listed formula and use the conjunction in parentheses if one is required. Be sure to include punctuation where it is needed.
2. Do the "S" Step of the "PENS" Strategy on the new clause that you have written.
3. Mark each complete verb in the new clause with a "V."
4. Mark each main subject in the new clause with an "S."

EXAMPLE:

D,I,cI
(for)

0. Although I am tired, I will walk home, for I cannot afford to be late.

			Formulas & Conjunctions		
M	C	V&S			
☐	☐	☐	ID,cI (but)	1.	Hanni works at the video arcade because she wants to earn money_____
☐	☐	☐	I;ID (after)	2.	You will have to help us; the car got stuck _____
☐	☐	☐	ID;I	3.	Janet left before I could stop her _____
☐	☐	☐	ID,cI (and)	4.	The horse jumped when the man hit him _____
☐	☐	☐	I;ID (because)	5.	The store was crowded; everyone had come _____
☐	☐	☐	I,cID (unless)	6.	James will ride his moped, and I will ride my 10-speed bike _____
☐	☐	☐	D,I;I	7.	If you decide to come, let me know _____
☐	☐	☐	D,I,cI (so)	8.	Although he had made the decision, he was not happy _____
☐	☐	☐	I,cID (until)	9.	The meal was superb, but the service was horrible _____
☐	☐	☐	D,I;I	10.	After the air warmed up, the trees were in bloom _____

COMPOUND-COMPLEX SENTENCE
LESSON 2B

Name_____

Date_____

INSTRUCTIONS:
1. Complete each of the following sentences to make a compound-complex sentence. Match your sentence to the listed formula and use the conjunction in parentheses if one is required. Be sure to include punctuation where it is needed.
2. Do the "S" Step of the "PENS" Strategy on the new clause that you have written.
3. Mark each complete verb in the new clause with a "V."
4. Mark each main subject in the new clause with an "S."

EXAMPLE:

D,I,cI
(for)
   0. Although I am tired, I will walk home, for I cannot afford to be late.

			Formulas &
M	**C**	**V&S**	**Conjunctions**
☐	☐	☐	D,I,cI (nor)	1. Although she was running in the race, she did not practice hard_____
☐	☐	☐	ID;I	2. I would like to go swimming because I am so hot_____
☐	☐	☐	I;ID (even if)	3. The news is bleak; the campaign will not be successful_____
☐	☐	☐	I,cID (before)	4. The climb up the mountain was steep, and we were tired_____
☐	☐	☐	D,I,cI (and)	5. When we need to go, I will let you know_____
☐	☐	☐	I,cID (provided)	6. I called the band leader, and they will play for the dance_____
☐	☐	☐	I;ID (so that)	7. The job was hard; we worked all day_____
☐	☐	☐	D,I,cI (for)	8. Although summer is here, there is snow on the ground_____
☐	☐	☐	I,cID (as long as)	9. Peter was a champion swimmer, and Chuck was a champion hurdler___
☐	☐	☐	D,I;I	10. After the the sun went down, the sky was a beautiful sight_____

COMPOUND-COMPLEX SENTENCE
LESSON 2C

Name_____

Date_____

INSTRUCTIONS:
1. Complete each of the following sentences to make a compound-complex sentence. Match your sentence to the listed formula and use the conjunction in parentheses if one is required. Be sure to include punctuation where it is needed.
2. Do the "S" Step of the "PENS" Strategy on the new clause that you have written.
3. Mark each complete verb in the new clause with a "V."
4. Mark each main subject in the new clause with an "S."

EXAMPLE:	
D,I,cI (for)	0. Although I am tired, I will walk home, for I cannot afford to be late.

M	C	V&S	Formulas & Conjunctions	
☐	☐	☐	D,I,cI (or)	1. Because there is a conflict in your schedule, you will have to drop computer science_____
☐	☐	☐	I;ID (until)	2. The protesters were arrested; everything had been peaceful_____
☐	☐	☐	ID,cI (yet)	3. I would like to see the play since I have read so many good reviews about it_____
☐	☐	☐	D,I;I	4. When my dentist finishes the dental work, I will be happy_____
☐	☐	☐	I,cID (before)	5. The starting players were introduced, and the anthem was sung_____
☐	☐	☐	D,I,cI (nor)	6. Until he called, I did not know the meeting time_____
☐	☐	☐	I,cID (when)	7. Jen and Jan will go shopping, and I will go to the park_____
☐	☐	☐	I;ID (if)	8. The race will begin at 9:00 A.M.; you must be there by 8:30 A.M._____
☐	☐	☐	I,cID (because)	9. The students listened carefully, but they could not understand the information_____
☐	☐	☐	ID;I	10. I honestly do not know when they will arrive_____

COMPOUND-COMPLEX SENTENCE
LESSON 2D

Name_____

Date_____

INSTRUCTIONS:
1. **Complete each of the following sentences to make a compound-complex sentence. Match your sentence to the listed formula and use the conjunction in parentheses if one is required. Be sure to include punctuation where it is needed.**
2. **Do the "S" Step of the "PENS" Strategy on the new clause that you have written.**
3. **Mark each complete verb in the new clause with a "V."**
4. **Mark each main subject in the new clause with an "S."**

EXAMPLE:	
D,I,cI (for)	0. Although I am tired, I will walk home, for I cannot afford to be late.

M	C	V&S	Formulas & Conjunctions	
☐	☐	☐	ID,cI (but)	1. Larry and Bob worked on the project until they were exhausted _____
☐	☐	☐	I,cID (since)	2. Julie asked me for help on her test, but I refused _____
☐	☐	☐	D,I,cI (and)	3. If we get the money, we will let you know_____
☐	☐	☐	ID;I	4. Gary hopes to go to college after he finishes high school _____
☐	☐	☐	I,cID (as)	5. The world watched, and the newsmen were silent _____
☐	☐	☐	ID,cI (or)	6. Donna can pick you up after you have finished working_____
☐	☐	☐	I,cID (when)	7. Paul called the meeting to order, and the men stopped talking _____
☐	☐	☐	D,I,cI (nor)	8. Unless something changes, Joe will not be able to go_____
☐	☐	☐	D,I;I	9. Because the light was good, the artist painted all morning _____
☐	☐	☐	I;ID (while)	10. The fog covered everything for miles; we were stranded _____

COMPOUND-COMPLEX SENTENCE
LESSON 3A

Name_____

Date_____

INSTRUCTIONS:
1. Complete each of the following sentences to make a compound-complex sentence. Match your sentence to the listed formula and use the listed conjunctions. Be sure to include punctuation where it is needed.
2. Do the "S" Step of the "PENS" Strategy on each sentence.
3. Mark each complete verb in the added clauses with a "V."
4. Mark each main subject in the new clauses with "S."

EXAMPLE:

I,cID   0. The plane dived toward the earth, $\overset{S}{\text{and}}$ $\overset{V}{\text{we saw}}$ an explosion $\overset{S}{\text{after}}$ $\overset{V}{\text{it hit}}$
(and, after)   the ground.

M	C	V&S	Formulas & Conjunctions
☐	☐	☐	D,I,cI 1. When the clock strikes nine _____ (or) _____
☐	☐	☐	I,cID 2. Jan cannot come over _____ (nor, unless) _____
☐	☐	☐	D,I;I 3. Although we are good friends _____ _____
☐	☐	☐	I,cID 4. Peter is a great sports fan _____ (yet, because) _____
☐	☐	☐	ID,cI 5. He went shopping _____ (before, so) _____
☐	☐	☐	I,cID 6. Eleanor has the measles _____ (and, since) _____
☐	☐	☐	D,I,cI 7. Since we have seven puppies _____ (but) _____
☐	☐	☐	ID;I 8. The milkman dropped his basket of bottles _____ (when) _____
☐	☐	☐	I;ID 9. The kitten lapped up the milk _____ (even though) _____
☐	☐	☐	ID,cI 10. Paul painted all afternoon _____ (after, for) _____

COMPOUND-COMPLEX SENTENCE
LESSON 3B

Name_____

Date_____

INSTRUCTIONS:
1. Complete each of the following sentences to make a compound-complex sentence. Match your sentence to the listed formula and use the listed conjunctions. Be sure to include punctuation where it is needed.
2. Do the "S" Step of the "PENS" Strategy on each sentence.
3. Mark each complete verb in the added clauses with a "V."
4. Mark each main subject in the new clauses with "S."

EXAMPLE:	S V S V
I,cID 0.	The plane dived toward the earth, *and we saw an explosion after it hit*
(and, after)	*the ground.*

M   C   V&S

Formulas & Conjunctions

☐ ☐ ☐   D,I;I   1.   Because we are late _____

_____

☐ ☐ ☐   ID,cI   2.   Jack is going motorcycling _____
             (although, and)

_____

☐ ☐ ☐   D,I;I   3.   If you will call _____

_____

☐ ☐ ☐   ID,cI   4.   The boys came early _____
             (since, but)

_____

☐ ☐ ☐   I,cID   5.   Don will coach the team _____
             (for, while)

_____

☐ ☐ ☐   D,I,cI   6.   After he had worked so hard _____
             (yet)

_____

☐ ☐ ☐   ID;I   7.   Fred tripped over the desk _____
             (after)

_____

☐ ☐ ☐   D,I,cI   8.   Unless you are willing to go now _____
             (nor)

_____

☐ ☐ ☐   I;ID   9.   The siren blew again and again _____
             (until)

_____

☐ ☐ ☐   D,I,cI   10.   Once you have started work _____
             (or)

_____

COMPOUND-COMPLEX SENTENCE
LESSON 3C

Name_____

Date_____

INSTRUCTIONS:
1. Complete each of the following sentences to make a compound-complex sentence. Match your sentence to the listed formula and use the listed conjunctions. Be sure to include punctuation where it is needed.
2. Do the "S" Step of the "PENS" Strategy on each sentence.
3. Mark each complete verb in the added clauses with a "V."
4. Mark each main subject in the new clauses with "S."

EXAMPLE:

I,cID   0. The plane dived toward the earth, <u>and we saw an explosion after it hit</u>
(and, after)   <u>the ground.</u>

(handwritten markings: S V over "we saw an explosion", S V over "it hit")

M	C	V&S	Formulas & Conjunctions	
☐	☐	☐	I,cID (yet, because)	1. The chair fell into the pool _____
☐	☐	☐	I;ID (unless)	2. He has to earn some money soon _____
☐	☐	☐	I,cID (so, when)	3. Let's try to finish early _____
☐	☐	☐	D,I;I	4. Unless you tell me _____
☐	☐	☐	ID,cI (after, but)	5. The teacher called the girls out of class _____
☐	☐	☐	ID;I (if)	6. Paul would run ten miles _____
☐	☐	☐	D,I,cI (and)	7. Although Adrian tried _____
☐	☐	☐	ID,cI (before, or)	8. Dean wants to go swimming _____
☐	☐	☐	ID;I (until)	9. The party was a great success _____
☐	☐	☐	D,I,cI (nor)	10. Once the fence is up _____

COMPOUND-COMPLEX SENTENCE
LESSON 3D

Name_____

Date_____

INSTRUCTIONS:
1. **Complete each of the following sentences to make a compound-complex sentence. Match your sentence to the listed formula and use the listed conjunctions. Be sure to include punctuation where it is needed.**
2. **Do the "S" Step of the "PENS" Strategy on each sentence.**
3. **Mark each complete verb in the added clauses with a "V."**
4. **Mark each main subject in the new clauses with "S."**

EXAMPLE: **I,cID** **(and, after)**	0. The plane dived toward the earth, _and we saw an explosion after it hit_ _the ground._

M	C	V&S	**Formulas &** **Conjunctions**		
☐	☐	☐	D,I;I	1.	If you finish your work immediately_____ _____
☐	☐	☐	D,I,cI (or)	2.	After you get done_____ _____
☐	☐	☐	ID;I (just as)	3.	The book was interesting_____ _____
☐	☐	☐	ID;I (whenever)	4.	Lenny will go waterskiing_____ _____
☐	☐	☐	I,cID (so, until)	5.	The birds will fly south_____ _____
☐	☐	☐	ID,cI (as if, for)	6.	Jesse pretended_____ _____
☐	☐	☐	D,I,cI (yet)	7.	When spring arrives_____ _____
☐	☐	☐	I;ID (as though)	8.	The brick mason rebuilt the chimney_____ _____
☐	☐	☐	I,cID (but, because)	9.	Larry gave me the money_____ _____
☐	☐	☐	I;ID (as long as)	10.	Terry rode horses all weekend_____ _____

COMPOUND-COMPLEX SENTENCE
LESSON 4A

Name_____

Date_____

INSTRUCTIONS:
1. For the first eight sentences, write compound-complex sentences to match the listed formulas. Use the conjunctions in parentheses as required.
2. For the last two sentences, pick your own compound-complex sentence formula from your Formula Card, write the formula on the blank to the left of the sentence, and write a matching sentence.
3. Remember to punctuate each sentence correctly and to check your work using the "S" Step of the "PENS" Strategy.

EXAMPLE:
I,cID   0. _The women left work early, for they want to eat_
(for, before)   _before the concert begins._

M	C	Formulas & Conjunctions	
☐	☐	D,I,cI (although, and)	1. _____
☐	☐	I,cID (or, if)	2. _____
☐	☐	ID,cI (when, but)	3. _____
☐	☐	D,I;I (because)	4. _____
☐	☐	ID;I (once)	5. _____
☐	☐	I;ID (even though)	6. _____
☐	☐	D,I,cI (unless, for)	7. _____
☐	☐	ID;I (since)	8. _____
☐	☐	_____	9. _____
☐	☐	_____	10. _____

COMPOUND-COMPLEX SENTENCE
LESSON 4B

Name_____

Date_____

INSTRUCTIONS:
1. **For the first eight sentences, write compound-complex sentences to match the listed formulas. Use the conjunctions in parentheses as required.**
2. **For the last two sentences, pick your own compound-complex sentence formula from your Formula Card, write the formula on the blank to the left of the sentence, and write a matching sentence.**
3. **Remember to punctuate each sentence correctly and to check your work using the "S" Step of the "PENS" Strategy.**

EXAMPLE:
I,cID   0. _The women left work early, for they want to eat_
(for, before)   _before the concert begins._

M	C	Formulas & Conjunctions	
☐	☐	D,I,cI (while, and)	1. _____
☐	☐	ID;I (after)	2. _____
☐	☐	ID,cI (as, so)	3. _____
☐	☐	D,I;I (once)	4. _____
☐	☐	I,cID (but, because)	5. _____
☐	☐	I;ID (until)	6. _____
☐	☐	D,I,cI (even if, nor)	7. _____
☐	☐	I,cID (yet, if)	8. _____
☐	☐	_____	9. _____
☐	☐	_____	10. _____

84

COMPOUND-COMPLEX SENTENCE
LESSON 4C

Name_____

Date_____

INSTRUCTIONS:
1. **For the first eight sentences, write compound-complex sentences to match the listed formulas. Use the conjunctions in parentheses as required.**
2. **For the last two sentences, pick your own compound-complex sentence formula from your Formula Card, write the formula on the blank to the left of the sentence, and write a matching sentence.**
3. **Remember to punctuate each sentence correctly and to check your work using the "S" Step of the "PENS" Strategy.**

EXAMPLE:	
I,cID 0.	_The women left work early, for they want to eat_
(for, before)	_before the concert begins._

M   C   **Formulas & Conjunctions**

☐ ☐   D,I,cI   1. _____
(although, so)
_____

☐ ☐   D,I;I   2. _____
(after, nor)
_____

☐ ☐   ID,cI   3. _____
(when, and)
_____

☐ ☐   ID;I   4. _____
(provided)
_____

☐ ☐   I,cID   5. _____
(but, unless)
_____

☐ ☐   I;ID   6. _____
(since)
_____

☐ ☐   I,cID   7. _____
(or, before)
_____

☐ ☐   D,I,cI   8. _____
(until, for)
_____

☐ ☐   _____   9. _____
_____

☐ ☐   _____   10. _____
_____

COMPOUND-COMPLEX SENTENCE
LESSON 4D

Name_____

Date_____

INSTRUCTIONS:

1. **For the first eight sentences, write compound-complex sentences to match the listed formulas. Use the conjunctions in parentheses as required.**
2. **For the last two sentences, pick your own compound-complex sentence formula from your Formula Card, write the formula on the blank to the left of the sentence, and write a matching sentence.**
3. **Remember to punctuate each sentence correctly and to check your work using the "S" Step of the "PENS" Strategy.**

EXAMPLE: I,cID (for, before)	0. _The women left work early, for they want to eat before the concert begins._

M C   **Formulas & Conjunctions**

☐ ☐ I,cID (and, even if) 1. _____

☐ ☐ ID,cI (until, for) 2. _____

☐ ☐ D,I,cI (when, yet) 3. _____

☐ ☐ D,I;I (while) 4. _____

☐ ☐ I,cID (but, so that) 5. _____

☐ ☐ ID;I (unless) 6. _____

☐ ☐ ID,cI (before, so) 7. _____

☐ ☐ D,I;I (once) 8. _____

☐ ☐ _____ 9. _____

☐ ☐ _____ 10. _____

COMPOUND-COMPLEX SENTENCE
LESSON 5A

Name_____

Date_____

INSTRUCTIONS:
1. **For each sentence, underline each <u>independent clause</u> with two lines.**
2. **Underline each <u>dependent clause</u> with one line.**
3. **In the blank to the left of each sentence, write the correct sentence formula for the sentence. Choose the correct formula from your Formula Card.**

EXAMPLE:

D,I, cI   0. Although I need the money, I will not steal, nor will I borrow.

F   L   Formulas

☐ ☐   _____   1. Linda and Terri were upset by the rude comment.

☐ ☐   _____   2. The fans clapped and cheered loudly; their team had entered the stadium.

☐ ☐   _____   3. We will not leave until you are ready.

☐ ☐   _____   4. If we work now, maybe we can go to the show later, but we may be too tired.

☐ ☐   _____   5. Hopefully, the rain will come, and we will not have to water the lawn.

☐ ☐   _____   6. If you agree, you should let her know.

☐ ☐   _____   7. He already has about five speeding tickets.

☐ ☐   _____   8. This afternoon we went to the swimming pool and swam a few laps.

☐ ☐   _____   9. Since the sky was so dark, Paul stopped painting; he had decided to finish the work tomorrow.

☐ ☐   _____   10. Before he got away, the reporter asked for an interview.

COMPOUND-COMPLEX SENTENCE
LESSON 5B

Name_____

Date_____

INSTRUCTIONS:
1. **For each sentence, underline each <u>independent clause</u> with two lines.**
2. **Underline each <u>dependent clause</u> with one line.**
3. **In the blank to the left of each sentence, write the correct sentence formula for the sentence. Choose the correct formula from your Formula Card.**

EXAMPLE:

_____ 0. <u>Although I need the money</u>, <u>I will not steal</u>, <u>nor will I borrow</u>.

F   L   Formulas

☐ ☐   _____   1. You have several courses from which to choose; you also have to take some required courses.

☐ ☐   _____   2. Could you and Bill pick up the laundry and drop off the cleaning?

☐ ☐   _____   3. Rick wanted to go out with Tony and Andy, yet he had a term paper to write.

☐ ☐   _____   4. You should decide if you want to go.

☐ ☐   _____   5. Before you make your decision, you better think about the alternatives, and you better consider the consequences.

☐ ☐   _____   6. Tina's friends took us to the concert and escorted us home.

☐ ☐   _____   7. At the job fair there were many employers; Todd talked to all of them.

☐ ☐   _____   8. We wanted to stay because we were having so much fun, but we had to be home by 1 A.M.

☐ ☐   _____   9. Although the application was long, I filled out the papers; I wanted the job badly.

☐ ☐   _____   10. The teachers organized a union, and they lobbied for pay increases.

COMPOUND-COMPLEX SENTENCE
LESSON 5C

Name_____

Date_____

INSTRUCTIONS:
1. **For each sentence, underline each <u>independent clause</u> with two lines.**
2. **Underline each <u>dependent clause</u> with one line.**
3. **In the blank to the left of each sentence, write the correct sentence formula for the sentence. Choose the correct formula from your Formula Card.**

EXAMPLE:

<u>D,I,cI</u>   0. <u>Although I need the money,</u> <u>I will not steal,</u> <u>nor will I borrow.</u>

F   L   Formulas

☐ ☐   _____   1. The wind blew strongly while the rain tossed our boat; the storm would last a long time.

☐ ☐   _____   2. Jeannie went to pick Paul up and drove him home.

☐ ☐   _____   3. Unemployment has risen sharply in the last year, and money has become tighter.

☐ ☐   _____   4. If we find a cure for cancer, thousands of lives could be saved each year.

☐ ☐   _____   5. Dean and Chris looked longingly at the motorcycle and dreamed of owning it.

☐ ☐   _____   6. The nature hike will be postponed until clear weather begins, but it will still be two days long.

☐ ☐   _____   7. Although the mail came today, no letter or package arrived.

☐ ☐   _____   8. After he ran quickly from the scene of the crime, the gangster got away, and the police were baffled.

☐ ☐   _____   9. The girls decided to have a party before school ends.

☐ ☐   _____   10. We could still see a shadow of the moon during the eclipse; it was a beautiful sight.

COMPOUND-COMPLEX SENTENCE
LESSON 5D

Name_____

Date_____

INSTRUCTIONS:
1. For each sentence, underline each <u>independent clause</u> with two lines.
2. Underline each <u>dependent clause</u> with one line.
3. In the blank to the left of each sentence, write the correct sentence formula for the sentence. Choose the correct formula from your Formula Card.

EXAMPLE:

<u>D, I, cI</u>   0. <u>Although I need the money</u>, <u>I will not steal</u>, <u>nor will I borrow</u>.

F   L   Formulas

☐ ☐   _____   1. When the bell rings, it will be time to leave for lunch.

☐ ☐   _____   2. Jerry wanted to rent a boat, so he went down to the dock early.

☐ ☐   _____   3. The speaker went on for two hours until a person in the audience interrupted, and we were happy to have a break.

☐ ☐   _____   4. Marilyn would like to leave now.

☐ ☐   _____   5. The great blue whale is the largest mammal alive, but the killer whale is the most dangerous and the deadliest.

☐ ☐   _____   6. Our car ran smoothly until we forgot to get a tune-up.

☐ ☐   _____   7. Kerry went to look at the bicycles; he had worked all summer in order that he could save enough money for one.

☐ ☐   _____   8. You might as well press your shirt while the iron is hot.

☐ ☐   _____   9. Linda drove over to Kansas City to see the Chinese Art Exhibit at the Nelson Art Gallery.

☐ ☐   _____   10. The students were quiet until the players entered, for they had heard rumors about suspensions from the team.

COMPOUND-COMPLEX SENTENCE
LESSON 6A

Name_____

Date_____

INSTRUCTIONS:
1. **For the first six items, write a sentence that matches the listed formula. Use the conjunctions in parentheses, and be sure to punctuate the sentence correctly.**
2. **For the last four items, choose a formula, write the formula on the blank, and write a sentence that matches the formula.**
3. **Use the "S" Step of the "PENS" Strategy on each sentence to check it.**

EXAMPLE: I;ID (since)	0. Ray and Kathy will join us later; they have to work late since the season is busy.

M C	Formulas & Conjunctions	
☐ ☐	S VV	1. _____ _____
☐ ☐	I,cI (but)	2. _____ _____
☐ ☐	ID (when)	3. _____ _____
☐ ☐	D,I;I (if)	4. _____ _____
☐ ☐	I,cID (and, after)	5. _____ _____
☐ ☐	D,I (although)	6. _____ _____
☐ ☐	Simple: _____	7. _____ _____
☐ ☐	Compound: _____	8. _____ _____
☐ ☐	Complex: _____	9. _____ _____
☐ ☐	Compound- complex: _____	10. _____ _____

COMPOUND-COMPLEX SENTENCE
LESSON 6B

Name_____

Date_____

INSTRUCTIONS:
1. **For the first six items, write a sentence that matches the listed formula. Use the conjunctions in parentheses, and be sure to punctuate the sentence correctly.**
2. **For the last four items, choose a formula, write the formula on the blank, and write a sentence that matches the formula.**
3. **Use the "S" Step of the "PENS" Strategy on each sentence to check it.**

EXAMPLE:	
I;ID 0.	_Ray and Kathy will join us later; they have to work late_
(since)	_since the season is busy._

M   C   Formulas & Conjunctions

☐ ☐ SS VV   1. _____

_____

☐ ☐ I;I   2. _____

_____

☐ ☐ D,I (since)   3. _____

_____

☐ ☐ I;ID (while)   4. _____

_____

☐ ☐ S VV   5. _____

_____

☐ ☐ ID,cI (before, yet)   6. _____

_____

☐ ☐ Simple: 7. _____

_____   _____

☐ ☐ Compound: 8. _____

_____   _____

☐ ☐ Complex: 9. _____

_____   _____

☐ ☐ Compound-complex: 10. _____

_____   _____

COMPOUND-COMPLEX SENTENCE
LESSON 6C

Name_____

Date_____

INSTRUCTIONS:
1. For the first six items, write a sentence that matches the listed formula. Use the conjunctions in parentheses, and be sure to punctuate the sentence correctly.
2. For the last four items, choose a formula, write the formula on the blank, and write a sentence that matches the formula.
3. Use the "S" Step of the "PENS" Strategy on each sentence to check it.

EXAMPLE:	
I;ID (since)	0. _Ray and Kathy will join us later; they have to work late since the season is busy._

M C

Formulas & Conjunctions

☐ ☐ S VV   1. _____

_____

☐ ☐ ID (even if)   2. _____

_____

☐ ☐ I,cI (for)   3. _____

_____

☐ ☐ ID,cI (as, so)   4. _____

_____

☐ ☐ D,I (once)   5. _____

_____

☐ ☐ D,I;I (unless) 6. _____

_____

☐ ☐ Simple: 7. _____

_____

☐ ☐ Compound: 8. _____

_____

☐ ☐ Complex: 9. _____

_____

☐ ☐ Compound- 10. _____
complex:

_____

COMPOUND-COMPLEX SENTENCE
LESSON 6D

Name_____

Date_____

INSTRUCTIONS:
1. For the first six items, write a sentence that matches the listed formula. Use the conjunctions in parentheses, and be sure to punctuate the sentence correctly.
2. For the last four items, choose a formula, write the formula on the blank, and write a sentence that matches the formula.
3. Use the "S" Step of the "PENS" Strategy on each sentence to check it.

EXAMPLE: I;ID (since)	0. _Ray and Kathy will join us later; they have to work late since the season is busy._

	Formulas &	
M	**C**	**Conjunctions**	
☐	☐	SS V	1. _____
			_____
☐	☐	I;I	2. _____
			_____
☐	☐	D,I (until)	3. _____
			_____
☐	☐	D,I,cI (because, nor)	4. _____
			_____
☐	☐	I,cI (or)	5. _____
			_____
☐	☐	ID;I (so that)	6. _____
			_____
☐	☐	Simple: _____	7. _____
			_____
☐	☐	Compound: _____	8. _____
			_____
☐	☐	Complex: _____	9. _____
			_____
☐	☐	Compound- complex: _____	10. _____
			_____

COMPOUND-COMPLEX SENTENCE
LESSON 7A, 7B, 7C, 7D (circle one)

Name_____

Date_____

INSTRUCTIONS:

1. In the space below, write at least six sentences about the topic listed on your Assignment Sheet. Include in this group of sentences at least one compound sentence, one complex sentence, and one compound-complex sentence. Use your Formula Card as needed.
2. Use the "S" Step of the "PENS" Strategy and a *Sentence Checklist* to check the kinds of sentences you have written.
3. Attach your completed *Sentence Checklist* to this sheet when you are done.

Topic: _____

_____

_____

_____

_____

_____

_____

_____

_____

_____

_____

_____

_____

_____

_____

_____

_____

_____

_____

_____

EVALUATION GUIDELINES

FOR THE LESSONS

EVALUATION GUIDELINES

Simple Sentence Lesson Series #1

See the appropriate answer key on page 111 or page 112.

Award for each sentence:

1 pt.   in the "F" column if the formula is correct.

1 pt.   in the "V" column if **all** the complete verbs are marked with a "V." (**No** partial credit should be given for marking one verb in a compound verb or for marking the main verb and not the helping verb or for marking the helping verb and not the main verb. **No** credit should be given for marking more than the complete verb [e.g., if the student marks the complete verb and an infinitive].)

1 pt.   in the "S" column if **all** of the main subjects are marked with an "S." (**No** partial credit should be given for marking one subject in a compound subject. **No** credit is given if more than one word is marked for each subject [e.g., if the student marks the subject and an adjective.])

Simple Sentence Lesson Series #2

Award for each sentence:

1 pt.   in the "M" column if the sentence matches the listed formula. (**No** partial credit is given for partially matching a formula.)

1 pt.   in the "C" column if the sentence is complete (no words left out) and correct (makes sense, has a period at the end).

1 pt.   in the "V&S" column if **all** of the subject(s) and verb(s) are identified correctly.*

Simple Sentence Lesson Series #3

Award for each sentence:

2 pts.   in the "M" column if the sentence matches the listed formula. (**No** partial credit should be given.)

1 pt.   in the "C" column if the sentence is complete and correct (i.e., no words are missing, the sentence makes sense, the first word has been capitalized, and end punctuation has been used).

---

*No partial credit should be given if the student marks one verb in a compound verb or one subject in a compound subject or marks part of a complete verb. **No** credit should be given if a student marks more words than is necessary (e.g., if the student marks the complete verb and an infinitive or marks the subject and an adjective).

Simple Sentence Lesson Series #4

Use the *Sentence Scoring Instructions* (Appendix A in the *Instructor's Manual*), a *Sentence Score Sheet* (Appendix B in the *Instructor's Manual*), and a *Sentence Checklist* (Appendix B in the *Instructor's Manual*) to score the student's work. Credit should **not** be given for a sentence if it has a missing word or words, does not make sense, or does not have a capitalized first word or end punctuation. All four types of simple sentences must be represented in the student's product. If the student writes a sentence that is more complicated than required (e.g., if the student writes a compound sentence), the student should receive credit for the sentence as long as it is complete and correct (i.e., no words missing, makes sense, etc.). This more complicated sentence may be accepted in place of a required sentence, as long as it contains the required form. For example, if the student writes a compound sentence that contains an independent clause that has a single subject and compound verb, this can be accepted in place of a simple sentence with a single subject and compound verb. However, this more complicated sentence should not be accepted in place of a required sentence if it does not contain the required form. For example, if the student writes a compound sentence having a total of two subjects and two verbs instead of a simple sentence with two subjects and two verbs, and no other sentence in the sample meets this requirement, the student has not fulfilled the mastery requirements.

Compound Sentence Lesson Series #1

See the appropriate answer key on page 113 or page 114.

Award for each sentence:

1 pt.   in the "F" column if the formula is correct.

1 pt.   in the "V" column if **all** of the complete verbs are each marked with a "V."*

1 pt.   in the "S" column if **all** of the main subjects are each marked with an "S."*

Compound Sentence Lesson Series #2

Award for each sentence:

1 pt.   in the "M" column if the sentence matches the listed formula. A comma and the listed coordinating conjunction or a semicolon must have been added as well as a subject and a verb. Partial credit should **not** be given if any of these requirements has not been met.

1 pt.   in the "C" column if the sentence is complete and correct (i.e., no words are missing, the sentence makes sense, the first word has been capitalized, and end punctuation has been used).

1 pt.   in the "V&S" column if **all** of the main subjects in the added clause are each marked with an "S" and **all** of the complete verbs in the added clause are each marked with a "V."*

---

*See the footnote on page 99.

Compound Sentence Lesson Series #3

Award for each sentence:

2 pts. in the "M" column if the sentence matches the listed formula. A comma and the listed coordinating conjunction or a semicolon must be in the sentence as required. Both clauses must have at least one subject and one verb. Partial credit should not be given if any of these requirements is not met.

1 pt. in the "C" column if the sentence is complete and correct. The sentence must have no missing words, must make sense, and must have beginning capitalization and end punctuation in order to receive this point of credit. (**No** partial credit is to be awarded.)

Compound Sentence Lesson Series #4

See the appropriate answer key on page 115 or page 116.

Award for each sentence:

1 pt. in the "F" column if the formula is correct.

1 pt. in the "V" column if **all** of the complete verbs are each marked with a "V."*

1 pt. in the "S" column if **all** of the main subjects are each marked with an "S."*

Compound Sentence Lesson Series #5

Award for each sentence:

2 pts. in the "M" column if the sentence matches the listed formula. A comma and the listed coordinating conjunction or a semicolon must be in the required compound sentences. (Partial credit should **not** be given for partially matching a formula.)

1 pt. in the "C" column if the sentence is complete and correct. The sentence must have no missing words, must make sense, and must have beginning capitalization and end punctuation in order to receive this point of credit. (**No** partial credit is to be awarded.)

---

*See the footnote on page 99.

Compound Sentence Lesson Series #6

Use the *Sentence Scoring Instructions* (Appendix A in the *Instructor's Manual*), a *Sentence Score Sheet* (Appendix B in the *Instructor's Manual*), and a *Sentence Checklist* (Appendix B in the *Instructor's Manual*) to score the student's work. Credit should **not** be given for a sentence if it has a missing word or words, does not make sense, or does not have a capitalized first word or end punctuation. Two types of simple sentences and the two types of compound sentences must be included in the student's product. If the student writes a sentence that is more complicated than those required (e.g., writes a compound-complex sentence), give credit for the sentence as long as it is complete and correct (e.g., no words missing, makes sense, etc.). This more complicated sentence may be used by the student in place of a required sentence, as long as it contains the simpler form. For example, if the student writes one compound sentence and one compound-complex sentence instead of the required two compound sentences, the student can reach mastery. However, the student who substitutes a complex sentence for a compound sentence should be required to do another lesson.

Complex Sentence Lesson Series #1

See the appropriate answer key on page 117 or page 118.

Award for each sentence:

2 pts. in the "F" column if the formula is correct.

1 pt. in the "L" column if the independent clause has two lines under it, <u>and</u> the dependent clause has one line under it. (**No** partial credit should be given if less than the whole clause is underlined. **No** credit should be given if more than the clause is underlined.)

Complex Sentence Lesson Series #2

Award for each sentence:

1 pt. in the "M" column if the sentence matches the listed formula. A comma and the listed subordinating conjunction must have been added, if necessary, as well as a subject and a verb. The added clause must make sense with the first clause. Partial credit should **not** be given if any of these requirements has not been met.

1 pt. in the "C" column if the sentence is complete and correct. The sentence must have no missing words, must make sense, and must have beginning capitalization and end punctuation in order to receive this point of credit. **No** partial credit is to be awarded.

1 pt. in the "V&S" column if **all** of the main subjects in the added clause are each marked with an "S" and **all** of the complete verbs in the added clause are each marked with a "V."*

---

*See the footnote on page 99.

Complex Sentence Lesson Series #3

Award for each sentence:

2 pts. in the "M" column if the sentence matches the listed formula. A comma and the listed subordinating conjunction must be in the sentence as required. Both clauses must have at least one subject and one verb. Partial credit should **not** be given if any of these requirements is not met.

1 pt. in the "C" column if the sentence is complete and correct. The sentence must have no missing words, must make sense, and must have beginning capitalization and end punctuation in order to receive this point of credit. (**No** partial credit is to be awarded.)

Complex Sentence Lesson Series #4

See the appropriate answer key on page 119 or page 120.

Award for each sentence:

2 pts. in the "F" column if the formula is correct.

1 pt. in the "L" column if the sentence is correctly underlined. Independent clauses must have two lines under them, and dependent clauses must have one line under them. (**No** partial credit should be given for partially underlining or for underlining more than the clause.)

Complex Sentence Lesson Series #5

Award for each sentence:

2 pts. in the "M" column if the sentence matches the listed formula. A comma and the listed subordinating or coordinating conjunction should be used as required. (Partial credit should **not** be given for partially matching a formula.)

1 pt. in the "C" column if the sentence is complete and correct. The sentence must have no missing words, must make sense, and must have beginning capitalization and end punctuation in order to receive this point of credit. (**No** partial credit is to be awarded.)

Complex Sentence Lesson Series #6

Use the *Sentence Scoring Instructions* (Appendix A in the *Instructor's Manual*), a *Sentence Checklist* (Appendix B in the *Instructor's Manual*), and a *Sentence Checklist* (Appendix B in the *Instructor's Manual*) to score the student's work. Credit should **not** be given for a sentence if it has a missing word or words, does not make sense, or does not have a capitalized first word or end punctuation. The student's product must contain at least one compound sentence and two complex sentences. The remaining sentences can be simple sentences. If the student writes a sentence that is more complicated than those required (e.g., writes a compound-complex sentence), give credit for the sentence as long as it is complete and correct (e.g., no words missing, makes sense, etc.). This more complicated sentence may be used by the student in place of a required sentence as long as it contains the simpler form. For example, if the student writes one compound sentence, one complex sentence, and one compound-complex sentence instead of the required one compound sentence and two complex sentences, the student can reach mastery; however, the student who substitutes a compound sentence for a complex sentence should be required to do another lesson.

Compound-Complex Sentence Lesson Series #1

See the appropriate answer key on page 121 or page 122.

Award for each sentence:

2 pts.   in the "F" column if the formula is correct.

1 pt.   in the "L" column if each independent clause had two lines under it, and the dependent clause has one line under it. (**No** partial credit should be given if less than the whole clause is underlined. **No** credit should be given if more than the clause is underlined.)

Compound-Complex Sentence Lesson Series #2

Award for each sentence:

1 pt.   in the "M" column if the sentence matches the listed formula. Appropriate punctuation and the listed conjunction must have been added, if necessary, as well as a subject and a verb. (Partial credit should **not** be given if any of these requirements has not been met.)

1 pt.   in the "C" column if the sentence is complete and correct. The sentence must have no missing words, must make sense, and must have beginning capitalization and end punctuation in order to receive this point of credit. **No** partial credit is to be awarded.

1 pt.   in the "V&S" column if **all** of the main subjects and **all** of the complete verbs in the added clause are each marked appropriately.*

---

*See the footnote on page 99.

Compound-Complex Sentence Lesson Series #3

Award for each sentence:

1 pt.   in the "M" column if the sentence matches the listed formula. Appropriate punctuation and the listed conjunction must be in the sentence as required. Both clauses must have at least one subject and one verb. Partial credit should **not** be given if any of these requirements is not met.

1 pt.   in the "C" column if the sentence is complete and correct. The sentence must have no missing words, must make sense, and must have beginning capitalization and end punctuation in order to receive this point of credit. **No** partial credit is to be awarded.

1 pt.   in the "V&S" column if **all** of the main subjects and all of the complete verbs of the added clauses have been marked appropriately.*

Compound-Complex Sentence Lesson Series #4

Award for each sentence:

2 pts.   in the "M" column if the sentence matches the listed formula. Appropriate punctuation and the listed conjunctions should be used as required. (Partial credit should **not** be given for partially matching a formula.)

1 pt.   in the "C" column if the sentence is complete and correct. The sentence must have no missing words, must make sense, and must have beginning capitalization and end punctuation in order to receive this point of credit. (**No** partial credit is to be awarded.)

Compound-Complex Sentence Lesson Series #5

See the appropriate answer key on page 123 or page 124.

Award for each sentence:

2 pts.   in the "F" column if the formula is correct.

1 pt.   in the "L" column if the clauses are correctly underlined. Independent clauses must have two lines under them, and dependent clauses must have one line under them. (**No** partial credit should be given for partially underlining or for underlining more than the clause.)

---

*See the footnote on page 99.

Compound-Complex Sentence Lesson Series #6

Award for each sentence:

2 pts.   in the "M" column if the sentence matches the listed formula. Appropriate punctuation and the listed conjunctions should be used as required. (Partial credit should **not** be given for partially matching a formula.)

1 pt.   in the "C" column if the sentence is complete and correct. The sentence must have no missing words, must make sense, and must have beginning capitalization and end punctuation in order to receive this point of credit. (**No** partial credit is to be awarded.)

Compound-Complex Sentence Lesson Series #7

Use the *Sentence Scoring Instructions* (Appendix A in the *Instructor's Manual*), a *Sentence Score Sheet* (Appendix B in the *Instructor's Manual*) and a *Sentence Checklist* (Appendix B in the *Instructor's Manual*) to score the student's work. Credit should **not** be given for a sentence if it has a missing word or words, does not make sense, or does not have a capitalized first word or end punctuation. The six sentences must be complete and must include at least one compound sentence, one complex sentence, and one compound-complex sentence.

ANSWER KEYS

FOR THE QUIZZES

AND LESSONS

ANSWER KEYS FOR THE QUIZZES

One point is awarded for each listed item in the box next to the item. Answers provided in parentheses are also acceptable. A total of 30 points are possible on each quiz. No partial credit is given. Points **should not** be taken off for spelling errors.

Simple Sentence Quiz

1. one (or 1)
2. subject
3. verb (predicate)
4. snow
5. runs
6. kitten
7. are playing
8. fell
9. rain
10. are
11. shoes
12. Is coming
13. Candy
14. dogs (S)
    cats (S)
15. Scott (S)
    Bill (S)
    Jeff (S)
16. man (S)
    grandson (S)
17. barked (V)
    yelped (V)
18. read (V)
    graded (V)
19. gulped (V)
    dashed (V)
20. witches (S)
    cats (S)
    surrounded (V)
    looked (V)

Compound Sentence Quiz

1. one (1)
2. two (2)
3. subject
4. verb (predicate)
5. Helen helped*
6. Mary refused (but Mary refused)*
7. Lee teaches math*
8. his wife teaches history
   (and his wife teaches history)*
9. but (yet)
10. for
11. so
12. and
13. nor
14. or
15. yet (but)
16. . . .sale, and. . .
17. . . .tag, but. . .
18. . . .freezer, so. . .
19. . . .Kathy, for. . .
20. . . .math; his. . .
21. . . .upstream; they. . .
22. . . .served; the. . .
23. . . .melting; it. . .
24. No comma should be added.**
25. No comma should be added.**
26. . . .fell, and. . .
27. . . .green, and. . . .
28. No comma should be added.**
29. . . .Devils, for. . . .
30. No comma should be added.**

---

* If the answers are reversed to #5 and #6 or to #7 and #8, this is acceptable.
**A point should be awarded only if no comma has been added.

Complex Sentence Quiz

1. one (1)
2. two (2)
3. one (1)
4. one (1)
5. independent
6. dependent
7. because she had a fever
8. If the weather is nice
9. subject
   verb (predicate)
10. until the alarm rings
11. rings
12. alarm
13. subject (complete verb or
    helping verb)
14. although
15. subordinating conjunction
16. dependent (independent)
    independent (dependent)
17. because
18. relationship
19. <u>I will go to the store</u> <u>after I make a shopping list.</u>
20. <u>When he eats his food,</u> <u>the dog gets meat all over his face.</u>
21. <u>Since she is my closest friend,</u> <u>I will buy something special for her birthday.</u>
22. No comma should be inserted.*
23. . . .student, he will. . .
24. No comma should be inserted.*
25. . . .decided, please. . .
26. No comma should be inserted.*
27. . . .skating, the guys. . .
28. . . .done, the four. . .

Compound-Complex Sentence Quiz

1. one
2. two
3. one
   one
4. two
   one
5. independent
6. dependent
7. <u>When they were late,</u> <u>the boss got angry, and they had to work overtime.</u>
8. <u>The girls stayed out</u> <u>until the moon had risen,</u> <u>so they got in trouble with their parents.</u>
9. <u>Anna scraped,</u> <u>and Tony sanded</u> <u>while I went to buy some paint.</u>
10. comma (,)
11. semicolon (;)
12. comma (,)
13. . . .innocence, we. . .
    . . .try you, and. . .
14. . . .is over, so. . .
15. . . .very good, sometimes. . .
    . . .place, and sometimes. . .
16. . . .Kathy went, she. . .
    . . .salad, and. . .
17. . . .moved away, but. . .
18. . . .need help, we. . .
    . . .Pete; he. . .

*A point should be awarded only if no comma has been added.

LESSON ANSWER KEYS

Simple Sentence Lesson 1A

	FORMULA	SUBJECT	SUBJECT	VERB	VERB
1.	S V	man		walked	
2.	SS V	boys	girls	were running	
3.	S VV	dog		chased	bit
4.	S V	girl		ran	
5.	SS VV	mother	father	came	comforted
6.	S VV	father		called	chased
7.	SS V	he	man	caught	
8.	SS V	leaves	branches	are	
9.	S VV	Chicago		is located	has
10.	SS VV	bravery	courage	are shown	are found

Simple Sentence Lesson 1B

	FORMULA	SUBJECT	SUBJECT	VERB	VERB
1.	S VV	girls		went	left
2.	SS V	man	woman	were married	
3.	S V	dishonesty		disgusted	
4.	SS VV	Jeff	Rick	threw	caught
5.	SS VV	Kathy	Bill	went	ate
6.	S VV	horse		jumped	kicked
7.	S VV	London		has become	has
8.	SS V	man	woman	yelled	
9.	S VV	parks		are scattered	attract
10.	SS V	James	Scott	go	

Simple Sentence Lesson 1C

	FORMULA	SUBJECT	SUBJECT	VERB	VERB
1.	SS V	pie	cookies	disappeared	
2.	S VV	boy		ate	got
3.	SS V	You	James	could come	
4.	S VV	people		danced	ate
5.	SS V	paperboy	milkman	come	
6.	S V	success		will depend	
7.	SS VV	Mary	I	are	want
8.	S V	Chip		went	
9.	SS V	Illness	loneliness	are	
10.	SS VV	Rick	girlfriend	had	walked

Simple Sentence Lesson 1D

	FORMULA	SUBJECT	SUBJECT	VERB	VERB
1.	S V	I		should have	
2.	S VV	beetles		could have flown	landed
3.	S V	plane		dived	
4.	S VV	Beauty		is	can be misjudged
5.	SS VV	France	England	had	fought
6.	SS V	spaceman	friends	sipped	
7.	S V	brother		sleeps	
8.	SS V	snake	toad	were	
9.	SS VV	Jonathan	Maria	ate	drank
10.	S VV	Fred		threw	blocked

Compound Sentence Lesson 1A

		SUBJECT	VERB	SUBJECT	VERB
1.	I,cI	snow	was falling	wind	was howling
2.	I;I	Nothing	could be done	air	had frozen
3.	I;I	Jake	got	Mac	grabbed
4.	I,cI	pair	pounded	it	would crack
5.	I,cI	Jenna	lit	ice	would melt
6.	I,cI	friends	had	they	would freeze
7.	I;I	They	were shivering	temperature	was
8.	I,cI	Jenna	could bend	she	could feel
9.	I,cI	Jake	pried	they	rushed
10.	I,cI	group	made	they	needed

Compound Sentence Lesson 1B

		SUBJECT(S)	VERB	SUBJECT	VERB(S)
1.	I;I	Michel Burdett	went	day	was
2.	I,cI	sun	was shining	sky	was
3.	I,cI	hikers	were lost	they	had forgotten
4.	I,cI	Michel	seemed	Burdett	showed
5.	I,cI	couple	climbed	they	could see get
6.	I;I	Michel	unpacked	Burdett	started
7.	I,cI	climbers	were starving	they	saved
8.	I;I	pair	started	sun	was
9.	I;I	they	found	it	was hidden
10.	I,cI	sportsmen	got	hike	had taken

Compound Sentence Lesson 1C

		SUBJECT	VERB	SUBJECT	VERB(S)
1.	I;I	pool	opens	we	should go grab
2.	I,cI	Terry	hates	she	uses
3.	I;I	President	called	he	wants
4.	I,cI	Scott	took	he	has heard
5.	I;I	We	should go	they	have
6.	I,cI	team	is	team	seems
7.	I,cI	We	could play	we	could stay listen
8.	I,cI	parents	bought	they	refuse
9.	I,cI	practice	starts	you	should hurry
10.	I;I	Tina	will graduate	she	wants

Compound Sentence Lesson 1D

		SUBJECT	VERB	SUBJECT	VERB(S)
1.	I;I	game	is	team	got
2.	I;I	Chris	asked	she	turned is going
3.	I,cI	Carrie	wants	she	agreed
4.	I,cI	fire	was caused	it	began
5.	I,cI	We	saw	it	was
6.	I;I	cars	are	I	will be able
7.	I,cI	I	have been looking	I	can find
8.	I,cI	town	got	school	was cancelled
9.	I;I	People	are starving	we	need
10.	I,cI	parents	will allow	they	will allow

Compound Sentence Lesson 4A

		SUBJECT	VERB	SUBJECT	VERB(S)	VERB
1.	SS V	Rick		James	met	
2.	S VV	guys	went		lifted	
3.	I;I	Randy	rode	Jeff	tried	
4.	S VV	Linda	jumped		knocked	
5.	I,cI	serve	looked	judge	called	
6.	S VV	He	stayed		served	
7.	SS VV	Chiefs		Oilers	played	won
8.	I;I	Ron	has	cancer	has spread	
9.	S V	Sue	was swimming			
10.	I,cI	Linda	wanted	she	refused	

Compound Sentence Lesson 4B

		SUBJECT	VERB	SUBJECT	VERB(S)	VERB
1.	S VV	Rick	finished		started	
2.	I;I	hobby	is	I	do have	
3.	S VV	Jenna	laughed		glanced	
4.	SS VV	Lindsay		Michael	went	saw
5.	I;I	jury	did believe	they	found	
6.	I,cI	Scott	had	he	wanted	
7.	S V	James	offered			
8.	I,cI	police	arrived	burglar	was caught	
9.	S VV	They	questioned		searched	
10.	S V	men	went			

Compound Sentence Lesson 4C

		SUBJECT	VERB	SUBJECT	VERB(S)	VERB
1.	S VV	mailman	ran		delivered	
2.	I;I	dog	took	mailman	yelled	
3.	S V	He	jumped			
4.	SS VV	boys		girls	watched	whispered
5.	I;I	boy	ran	boy	called	
6.	I,cI	police	arrived	they	asked	
7.	I,cI	dog	belongs	he	will feed	
8.	SS V	Mr. Perkins		wife	live	
9.	I,cI	house	needs	family	is	
10.	I,cI	police	captured	they	put	

Compound Sentence Lesson 4D

		SUBJECT	VERB	SUBJECT	VERB	VERB
1.	SS V	Peter		friends	went	
2.	I,cI	Peter	was assigned	he	lost	
3.	S VV	He	searched		inspected	
4.	S V	group	had planned			
5.	I;I	Peter	was	he	sat	thought
6.	SS VV	brother		others	scolded	told
7.	I,cI	Peter	found	he	shouted	
8.	I;I	boys	sat	they	passed	
9.	S V	chicken	was			
10.	I,cI	picnic	was	stomachs	were	

Complex Sentence Lesson 1A

1.	ID	… <u>leaves myself</u> <u>unless you</u>…*
2.	D,I	…<u>went home,</u> <u>the band</u>…
3.	D,I	…<u>pace herself,</u> <u>she will</u>…
4.	ID	…<u>for me</u> <u>because I</u>…
5.	D,I	…<u>got warm,</u> <u>we have</u>…
6.	D,I	…<u>at me,</u> <u>my heart</u>…
7.	ID	…<u>for me</u> <u>while I</u>…
8.	D,I	…<u>boa constrictor,</u> <u>you should</u>…
9.	D,I	…<u>to death,</u> <u>Kathy gave</u>…
10.	ID	…<u>a home</u> <u>even if</u>…

Complex Sentence Lesson 1B

1.	D,I	…<u>was falling,</u> <u>the streets</u>…*
2.	D,I	…<u>this homework,</u> <u>we should</u>…
3.	ID	…<u>come tomorrow</u> <u>if he</u>…
4.	D,I	…<u>was noisy,</u> <u>he was</u>…
5.	ID	…<u>looked happy</u> <u>once her</u>…
6.	D,I	…<u>to study,</u> <u>he will</u>…
7.	ID	…<u>floppy hat</u> <u>as if</u>…
8.	D,I	…<u>lights on,</u> <u>we are</u>…
9.	D,I	…<u>were careful,</u> <u>we still</u>…
10.	D,I	…<u>best team,</u> <u>we may</u>…

---

*This answer key shows where the underlining should change. The students should be required to underline the whole clause.

Complex Sentence Lesson 1C

1.	D,I	…<u>stops soon</u>, <u>we will</u>…*
2.	D,I	…<u>fly south</u>, <u>winter is</u>…
3.	ID	…<u>basketball team</u> <u>although she</u>…
4.	D,I	…<u>on time</u>, <u>he can</u>…
5.	D,I	…<u>am nominated</u>, <u>I will</u>…
6.	ID	…<u>Carrie acts</u> <u>as if</u>…
7.	ID	…<u>The sky looks</u> <u>as though</u>…
8.	D,I	…<u>is smoke</u>, <u>there is</u>…
9.	D,I	…<u>in second</u>, <u>we felt</u>…
10.	ID	…<u>extra assignment</u> <u>so that</u>…

Complex Sentence Lesson 1D

1.	D,I	…<u>guest speaker</u>, <u>the school</u>…*
2.	ID	…<u>soccer team</u> <u>since he</u>…
3.	ID	…<u>as long</u> <u>because everyone</u>…
4.	D,I	…<u>finishes practicing</u>, <u>we can</u>…
5.	ID	…<u>the house</u> <u>before his</u>…
6.	D,I	…<u>in Florida</u>, <u>they got</u>…
7.	D,I	…<u>the game</u>, <u>winning will</u>…
8.	ID	…<u>stopped talking</u> <u>when the</u>…
9.	D,I	…<u>the costs</u>, <u>they can</u>…
10.	ID	…<u>the car</u> <u>if he</u>…

---

*This answer key shows where the underlining should change. The students should be required to underline the whole clause.

Complex Sentence Lesson 4A

1.	SS V	Jess and Rick took the bus to the concert.
2.	S V	Everyone had a good time.
3.	D,I	…to practice, you cannot…*
4.	I,cI	…demanded a lot, and the people…
5.	S V	The car was painted a bright blue.
6.	I,cI	…get pizza, but we…
7.	ID	…an agreement because their…
8.	I;I	…with us; they enjoyed…
9.	I,cI	…stay home, yet your…
10.	ID	…the doctor when she…

Complex Sentence Lesson 4B

1.	I,cI	…5:00 A.M., so we…*
2.	I;I	…work now; we will…
3.	ID	…be pruned until they…
4.	SS V	Books and newspapers can be found in the library or study.
5.	I,cI	…ride motorcycles, but his…
6.	ID	…thousand books before the…
7.	S VV	I grade a lot of quizzes and make up a lot of assignment sheets.
8.	D,I	…asked me, I will…
9.	SS VV	The peaches and plums smelled and tasted good.
10.	I,cI	…stay here, or you…

---

*This answer key shows where the underlining should change or be discontinued. The students should be required to underline the whole clause.

Complex Sentence Lesson 4C

1. D,I   …<u>over here</u>, <u>I will</u>…*
2. S VV   <u>Jerry gave Mary his pen and took it away.</u>
3. I,cI   …<u>the air</u>, <u>and Peter</u>…
4. ID   …<u>me up because I</u>…
5. D,I   …<u>the party</u>, <u>they did</u>…
6. I,cI   …<u>ate popcorn</u>, <u>and it</u>…
7. I,cI   …<u>a message</u>, <u>but I</u>…
8. SS VV   <u>The sandwiches and pop are here and are ready to be eaten.</u>
9. D,I   …<u>the problem</u>, <u>he found</u>…
10. SS VV   <u>Lila and Don ran and dived into the water.</u>

Complex Sentence Lesson 4D

1. ID   …<u>the fair if he</u>…*
2. S   V   <u>We went swimming at the lake last Saturday.</u>
3. I;I   …<u>algebra test</u>; <u>he did</u>…
4. ID   …<u>be 9:30 before we</u>…
5. S VV   <u>Running to the bus, David tripped and fell.</u>
6. SS VV   <u>Kim and David stopped working and started something else.</u>
7. D,I   …<u>Scott goes</u>, <u>James will</u>…
8. S   V   <u>Kathy works hard at school.</u>
9. I,cI   …<u>to go</u>, <u>yet he</u>…
10. D,I   …<u>came up</u>, <u>the boys</u>…

*This answer key shows where the underlining should change or be discontinued. The students should be required to underline the whole clause.

Compound-Complex Sentence Lesson 1A

1.	I,cID	...soon, <u>but I will not be disappointed</u> <u>if she</u>...*
2.	D,I;I	...<u>time,</u> <u>Tom will write his paper;</u> <u>he will</u>...
3.	I;ID	...<u>home;</u> <u>she has to babysit</u> <u>until her</u>...
4.	ID,cI	...<u>leave</u> <u>when Rick does,</u> <u>and Scott</u>...
5.	D,I,cI	...<u>hours,</u> <u>the girls finally came,</u> <u>and they</u>...
6.	ID;I	...<u>worked</u> <u>until the rain began;</u> <u>they huddled</u>...
7.	D,I,cI	...<u>done,</u> <u>they can go get Jim,</u> <u>and we</u>...
8.	ID,cI	...<u>power</u> <u>until he died,</u> <u>and his</u>...
9.	D,I;I	...<u>soon,</u> <u>we will have to leave;</u> <u>we should</u>...
10.	ID,cI	...<u>go</u> <u>because I really like to shop,</u> <u>but I</u>...

Compound-Complex Sentence Lesson 1B

1.	D,I,cI	...<u>left,</u> <u>George had eaten all the pizza,</u> <u>and Sam</u>...*
2.	I;ID	...<u>signed;</u> <u>six weeks had passed</u> <u>before the</u>...
3.	I,cID	...<u>early,</u> <u>so we will be sure to get tickets</u> <u>although the</u>...
4.	D,I,cI	...<u>downtown,</u> <u>Sam had a wreck,</u> <u>and the</u>...
5.	ID;I	...<u>Kim</u> <u>after he left work;</u> <u>he had</u>...
6.	ID,cI	...<u>book</u> <u>since it was the required assignment,</u> <u>but she</u>...
7.	D,I;I	...<u>work,</u> <u>we will have to fire you;</u> <u>we can</u>...
8.	D,I;I	...<u>dog,</u> <u>no one replied;</u> <u>they all</u>...
9.	I,cID	...<u>hard,</u> <u>and George worked even harder</u> <u>until the</u>...
10.	D,I,cI	...<u>cuts,</u> <u>many of the telephones were removed,</u> <u>and the</u>...

---

*This answer shows where the underlining should change or be discontinued. The students should be required to underline the whole clause.

Compound-Complex Sentence Lesson 1C

1.	I,cID	…<u>meal</u>, <u>and we all enjoyed it</u> <u>although we</u>…*
2.	I;ID	…<u>dollars</u>; <u>I will have to sell it</u> <u>unless you</u>…
3.	D,I;I	…<u>out</u>, <u>animal life will probably not survive</u>; <u>plant life</u>…
4.	D,I,cI	…<u>begun</u>, <u>there is no one outside</u>, <u>and all</u>…
5.	ID,cI	…<u>go</u> <u>before he got here</u>, <u>but he</u>…
6.	D,I,cI	…<u>team</u>, <u>his parents had to sign a permission slip</u>, <u>and he</u>…
7.	I;ID	…<u>course</u>; <u>it has the facilities necessary to hold a major golf tournament</u> <u>although none</u>…
8.	D,I,cI	…<u>soon</u>, <u>we will not have time to get to the store</u>, <u>nor will</u>…
9.	ID;I	…<u>tonight</u> <u>since the storm is so fierce</u>; <u>she can</u>…
10.	I,cID	…<u>gear</u>, <u>and he had all the menus planned</u> <u>although he</u>…

Compound-Complex Sentence Lesson 1D

1.	ID;I	…<u>crowded</u> <u>before the concert began</u>; <u>everyone had</u>…*
2.	D,I;I	…<u>car</u>, <u>Jan does not have enough money</u>; <u>Jean does</u>…
3.	ID,cI	…<u>weapons</u> <u>because many countries have developed them</u>, <u>but there</u> …
4.	I,cID	…<u>legislation</u>, <u>and the Congress passed it</u> <u>before anyone</u>…
5.	D,I,cI	…<u>late</u>, <u>the whole group missed the show</u>, <u>and everyone</u>…
6.	I,cID	…<u>it</u>, <u>yet this is not good</u> <u>since you</u>…
7.,	I;ID	…<u>smoking</u>; <u>this seems to have had little effect on cigarette sales</u> <u>because people</u>…
8.	I;ID	…<u>house</u>; <u>I wanted to buy it too</u> <u>after I</u>…
9.	D,I,cI	…<u>library</u>, <u>Karl drove her</u>, <u>so she</u>…
10.	D,I;I	…<u>sponsor</u>, <u>we will not be able to play in the league</u>; <u>our chances</u>…

---

*This answer key shows where the underlining should change or be discontinued. The students should be required to underline the whole clause.

Compound-Complex Sentence Lesson 5A

1.   SS   V   <u>Linda and Terry were upset by the rude comment</u>.
2.   I;I   …<u>cheered loudly</u>; <u>their team</u>…*
3.   ID   …<u>not leave</u> <u>until you</u>…
4.   D,I,cI   …<u>now</u>, <u>maybe we can go to the show later</u>, <u>but we may</u>…
5.   I,cI   …<u>will come</u>, <u>and we</u>…
6.   D,I   …<u>you agree</u>, <u>you should</u>…
7.   S   V   <u>He already has about five speeding tickets</u>.
8.   S   VV   <u>This afternoon we went to the swimming pool and swam a few laps</u>.
9.   D,I;I   …<u>dark</u>, <u>Paul stopped painting</u>; <u>he had</u>…
10.   D,I   …<u>got away</u>, <u>the reporter</u>…

Compound-Complex Sentence Lesson 5B

1.   I;I   …<u>to choose</u>; <u>you also</u>…*
2.   SS   VV   <u>Could you and Bill pick up the laundry and drop off the cleaning</u>?
3.   I,cI   …<u>Tony and Andy</u>, <u>yet he</u>…
4.   ID   …<u>should decide</u> <u>if you</u>…
5.   D,I,cI   …<u>decision</u>, <u>you better think about the alternatives</u>, <u>and you</u>…
6.   S   VV   <u>Tina's friends took us to the concert and escorted us home</u>.
7.   I;I   …<u>many employers</u>; <u>Todd talked</u>…
8.   ID,cI   …<u>stay</u> <u>because we were having so much fun</u>, <u>but we</u>…
9.   D,I;I   …<u>long</u>, <u>I filled out the papers</u>; <u>I wanted</u>…
10.   I,cI   …<u>a union</u>, <u>and they</u>…

---

*This answer key shows where the underlining should change or be discontinued. The students should be required to underline the whole clause.

Compound-Complex Sentence Lesson 5C

1.	ID;I	…strongly <u>while the rain tossed our boat</u>; <u>the storm</u>…*
2.	S VV	<u>Jeannie went to pick Paul up and drove him home.</u>
3.	I,cI	…<u>last year</u>, <u>and money</u>…
4.	D,I	…<u>for cancer</u>, <u>thousands of</u>…
5.	SS VV	<u>Dean and Chris looked longingly at the motorcycle and dreamed of owning it.</u>
6.	ID,cI	…postponed <u>until clear weather begins</u>, <u>but it</u>…
7.	D,I	…<u>came today</u>, <u>no letter</u>…
8.	D,I,cI	…<u>crime</u>, <u>the gangster got away</u>, <u>and the</u>…
9.	ID	…<u>a party</u> <u>before school</u>…
10.	I;I	…<u>the eclipse</u>; <u>it was</u>…

Compound-Complex Sentence Lesson 5D

1.	D,I	…<u>bell rings</u>, <u>it will</u>…*
2.	I,cI	…<u>a boat</u>, <u>so he</u>…
3.	ID,cI	…<u>hours until a person in the audience interrupted</u>, <u>and we</u>…
4.	S V	<u>Marilyn would like to leave now.</u>
5.	I,cI	…<u>mammal alive</u>, <u>but the</u>…
6.	ID	…<u>ran smoothly</u> <u>until we</u>…
7.	I;ID	…<u>bicycles</u>; <u>he had worked all summer</u> <u>in order that</u>…
8.	ID	…<u>your shirt</u> <u>while the</u>…
9.	S V	<u>Linda drove over to Kansas City to see the Chinese Art Exhibit at the Nelson Art Gallery.</u>
10.	ID,cI	…<u>quiet until the players entered</u>, <u>for they</u>…

---

*The answer key shows where the underlining should change or be discontinued. The students should be required to underline the whole clause.